X120

Tri-ang Toys

1937/38

**Plus an Addendum
for additional items
in the 1939/40 season.**

 New Cavendish Books

Our grateful thanks are due to Peggy and Richard Lines for their unstinting co-operation in providing material for this publication.

Peggy Lines is in the course of preparing a major history of the Lines family toy business.

The 1937/38 Tri-ang catalogue together with the Frog Aircraft Supplement used for the production of this book are amongst the few complete examples known. The catalogue with covering letter and price list were donated to The London Toy & Model Museum archive some years ago.

The page references in the 1936/37 price list that was included with the catalogue do not cross-reference with the 1937/38 catalogue.

This first edition published in Great Britain by New Cavendish Books – 1988

Printed and bound by Mandarin Offset

New Cavendish Books Ltd
23 Craven Hill, London W2 3EN.
01-262 7905/9450

ISBN 0 904568 71 7

CONTENTS

INTRODUCTION
by Richard Lines

The early history of the Lines family connection with toy making is not too well documented. George Lines (born 1841) set up as a rocking horse manufacturer in the 1870s and was joined by his brother Joseph (born 1848) soon after. On Joseph's marriage certificate of 30th June 1877 he describes himself as a rocking horse maker. The firm was called G. and J. Lines Ltd. and was a considerable success. Joseph bought out George's interest in 1903 and remained the boss until his death on 31st December 1931.

Joseph married Jane Fitzhenry and they had four sons and four daughters. When the sons were of suitable age (16-18) they joined the firm and learnt their trade from the bottom. This involved opening the factory in the morning, doing all the processes including the most unpleasant job of cleaning cows' tails (which were then 're-sited' at the rear of a rocking horse), making their own varnish, woodwork, office work and, when everyone else had gone home, locking up the factory. This was followed by night school study, suitable subjects being art and design.

Joe Lines, as he was called, was a fairly typical Victorian autocrat. It was said that 'The wages of sin is death' (an apparently ungrammatical quotation from Romans chapter 6 verse 23) and 'the wages of old Joe Lines is a ****** sight worse'. Doubtless such a statement was applicable to many other firms at the time and may even be in use today. Joe had a natural aversion to paying income tax and also being asked to account for his business expenses. When pressed he assessed one quarter to 'travelling north', one quarter to 'travelling south' and the balance to 'travelling west'. The omission of any eastward travel was intended to make the split less suspicious.

The firm had its Head Office in the Caledonian Road in the Kings Cross area of north London. In time it acquired several other small works round about. The four sons of Joseph were William Joseph (1879), Walter (1882), George Edward (1888) and Arthur Edwin (1892). The two elder ones took on some influence in the way the firm was run and shortly before the first war were able to persuade Joseph that all the small premises were uneconomic. They wanted to build a new, modern factory where everything would be under one roof. Their plan was eventually accepted and a new factory was purpose built at Down Lane, Tottenham and opened in 1914. When the war came, the three younger sons joined up, leaving William, who was over age, to stay on with Joseph.

All three survived the war while William had a rough time trying to keep the business going with a 70 year old father who was not keen on new ideas. After an excess of needless provocation he resigned in December 1918 and, with the others being demobilised, they decided to set up in business on their own. George elected to take up farming so the

three others formed a company which they called Lines Bros. Ltd. Their trade mark was a triangle, this being a simple construcion made up by three lines. The word Triangtois was also used and this was later abbreviated to a more pronounceable Tri-ang Toys. Joseph carried on G. and J. Lines Ltd. until his death in 1931. There was some friendly rivalry between the two companies and it is pleasing to record that once the split had taken place, the family resumed its previous good relations.

Lines Bros. (not 'brothers') Ltd. was formed in 1919 and the first factory was at Ormside Street, off the Old Kent Road in south east London. Operations began with unbelievable speed. With their previous experience it did not take long to design new toys and they had immediate connections with all the customers of G. and J. Lines. The market was short of toys after the war and they thus got off to a flying start. By 1921 it was necessary to acquire more space and another factory, No. 761 Old Kent Road, was purchased.

From the beginning, illustrated catalogues were produced and these included a number of coloured pages. The toys themselves were of high quality, largely of wood construction. Looking at the old pictures, every model seems to have been produced in numerous sizes. The first version would be categorised as No. 1. When larger sizes were introduced these became Nos. 2, 3, 4 etc. Smaller versions would be No. 0, 00, 000 etc. This practice can be traced back to the G. and J. Lines techniques of the 1890s. The use of pressed steel for toy making began early on as did such ancillary processes as stove enamelling and electro-plating. The Lines view of toy making was that you made everything possible yourself, so different from present day 'makers' who, faced with a problem, jump on a jumbo jet to 'source' whatever they can't make 'in the Orient'.

The relative talents of the brothers fitted together admirably. William was the salesman, Walter the designer, factory organiser and finance man while Arthur looked after the office and oiled the administration. William and Walter took it in turns to be the Chairman, an unusual arrangement. The other directors were G. M. Campbell, a brother-in-law of Walter, Ralph Freeman, another brother-in-law who had married Mary Lines and was a renowned civil engineer and R. C. Munro, a former school friend and also a highly talented engineer.

By 1923 it again became apparent that more space was needed. A splendid site was found at Merton, close to South Wimbledon underground station. In those days the area was comparatively undeveloped and the purchase of 20 acres, with an option on a further 27 acres, was made inexpensively. The first section of what was to become a major complex was a 170,000 sq. ft. building which was later to be known as the north factory. It was occupied in June 1924 and

From left to right, George, Edith (Dee), Walter, Arthur Edwin, Joseph Lines, William Joseph, Jane Lines (Fitzhenry), Winifred, Mary.
Silver Wedding 30 June 1902.

Walter, George and Arthur Lines at the wedding of their sister Edith, 7 June 1916.

represented an important step in the progress of the company. The opportunity was taken to install a great deal of up-to-date machinery and equipment which enabled the toys to be made at keen prices, thus in turn helping to increase the volume throughput.

Wood toys were still in the majority and the sawdust from the production of these was converted to 'producer gas' which fuelled the main factory boiler. In later years when many of these toys were made from steel, the output of nursery furniture, cots, high chairs, playpens etc. still provided sufficient fuel to make the cost of heating minimal.

In addition to the ever expanding ranges of toys, it is often overlooked that an important part of the business was the production of Pedigree Prams. Prams had also been made by G. and J. Lines and the reason behind them was that they were in demand in the spring when no one wanted toys and the demand fell off in the autumn, allowing the factory to concentrate on the toy season. The two products had many common production requirements and thus fitted together well.

It had long been the practice for pram and toy

makers to buy wheels from specialist manufacturers. Lines, however, invested large sums in setting up their own wheel plant using what, for those days, were highly automated methods. Presswork was another area where the company excelled. Large power presses capable of producing pram side panels were equally useful for pedal motor car bodies and such metal work was a great deal cheaper and more robust than the wooden bodies that had been the standard before. Other products which benefitted from the change to metal were such toys as scooters, wheelbarrows, lorries and engines.

As early as 1920, Walter applied for a patent on a juvenile bicycle which was marketed as the Fairy Cycle. This was an outstanding success and was heavily promoted in the national press. Warnings were published widely threatening action against anyone infringing the patents. Another item which became a perennial favourite was the Puff-Puff engine. It had a bellows attached to a cranked front axle and emitted a realistic engine noise when it was pulled along. Investigation has shown that this idea was submitted by a member of the public and one can only hope that he was adequately rewarded.

About 1928 Lines made their first acquisition. This was the Unique and Unity Cycle Co. Ltd. of Birmingham, a long established but run-down company. After due reorganisation to conform with Walter's ideas it became a highly successful performer and a new factory was built for it at Handsworth in 1935.

Shortly after, in 1931, the opportunity arose to acquire Hamleys in Regent Street. The business had been established by William Hamley in 1760. He came to London from Bodmin in Cornwall and set up shop in High Holborn. By 1900 it had several branches around London and the one in Regent Street fell due to be rebuilt, along with many other buildings in the street. The cost of this was too much for Hamleys and they struggled through to 1931 when a rescue became essential. Walter saw the possibilities, bought a majority holding and set to work to restore its fortunes. He took the precaution of asking other toy makers whether they would be willing to supply him and all were only too happy to think that they would now get paid promptly for their goods which had not previously been the case.

Early in 1932, Lines acquired a holding in a small company called International Model Aircraft Ltd. and the sole selling rights for its revolutionary ready-to-fly model aeroplane. This was named the FROG, an acronym for Flies Right Off the Ground. It proved to be a magnificent flier (and seller) and was followed by a variety of other models. In 1937, the FROG company introduced their Penguin plastic kits, the originals of what were to become almost an industry of their own some twenty years later.

Lines Bros. Ltd. became a public company on 7th June 1933 by the issue of 200,000 $5\frac{1}{2}$% First Preference Shares. The Ordinary Shares remained privately held until 1936, many of these having been

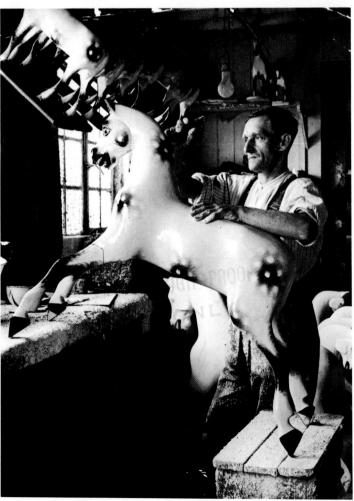

subscribed for by members of the large Lines family and friends. On going public, Mr. G. F. R. Baguley joined the Board to represent the outside interests and was a tremendous asset for the next thirty years.

The country was going through a depression in the 1930s and this led the Government to press manufacturers to produce items that had been traditionally imported. Most clockwork toys came from Germany and it was a bold man who felt he could take on the Germans at this game. However Lines Bros. Ltd. was prepared to have a go and in 1935 came out with a range of MINIC (Miniature Clockwork) vehicles, all to a common scale. They proved to be very popular and are now prized by collectors.

Similarly inspired by the Government, Lines went into soft toys in 1937 following these up with Pedigree Dolls in 1938. In this case a separate company was formed called Pedigree Soft Toys Ltd. which occupied the South Factory of the Merton complex.

Thus, in a mere twenty years, a major enterprise was built up. Its success revolved round the three brothers of whom, inevitably, a number of stories were told. William was an enthusiast for motor cars, shooting, skiing and, at an advancing age, deer stalking. Rushing into the office one morning, he called out to the commissionaire to put some water in his car. The commissionaire, an ex-cavalryman, was not too familiar with cars and could only find one place where water could enter. The resulting mixture of water and petrol did not please William.

Walter at work was something of a tiger. His office looked out on to the loading bank where the sight of two men pushing a barrow practically gave him apoplexy. He thereupon sacked everyone in sight (they were forgiven next morning) and set to work to design a barrow with which one man could manoeuvre umpteen tons. These were made within the company and woe betide any second pair of hands caught helping to push one.

Arthur was noted for his dry sense of humour. Someone having the temerity to crack a joke in his office would be told 'if there are to be any jokes in here, I will make them'. The brothers were all considerable characters and it was notable how few people left the firm once they had got the drift of the way things were done. A good performance from anyone could bring the reward of a new hat, perhaps a strange thing nowadays, but much appreciated then.

William Joseph Lines (second from left) with Arthur Lines pushing Tri-ang electric Rolls Royce on factory field with African visitors in summer 1933.

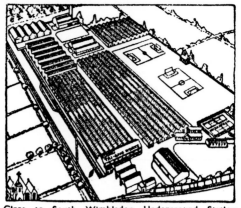

Close to South Wimbledon Underground Station
Edgware—Morden Line

The Largest in the **Toy Factory World**

TRI-ANG TOYS

OUR REF.................. YOUR REF...................

Lines Bros. Ltd.

DIRECTORS: W. J. LINES, WALTER LINES, A. E. LINES, G. M. CAMPBELL, R. C. MUNRO, R. FREEMAN, G. F. R. BAGULEY

TRI-ANG WORKS, MORDEN ROAD, MERTON, LONDON, S.W.19, ENGLAND

Telephone: **LIBERTY 4242**   *Telegrams:* **TRIANGTOIS, PHONE, LONDON**
(6 Lines)   (Code: Western Union, 5 letter)

City Showrooms: **18 NEW UNION ST., LONDON, E.C.2**   *Telephone:* **Met 0337**

Birmingham Branch: **UNIQUE & UNITY CYCLE CO., LTD.** (Prop.: Lines Bros. Ltd.)
CAMP LANE   *Telephone:* **Northern 1227**
HANDSWORTH

11th August, 1937.

Dear Sir/s,

We have pleasure in enclosing herewith our GENERAL TOY CATALOGUE NO. 39, 1937/38, and FROG Model Aircraft Catalogue No. 39A.

Improvements have been made to old favourites and new models added to the range of Childrens motors, dolls houses, desks, dolls prams etc.,

MINIC all-to-scale clockwork toys - A number of interesting new models have been added.

"FIT-BITS" - We draw your particular attention to the new range of constructional toys for children of all ages. THERE ARE NO SHARP EDGES OR METAL PARTS and each set is beautifully finished in a variety of colours.

You FIT the BITS together with Patented Rubber Connections. We are carrying out an extensive advertising campaign in Journals which appeal to Mothers.

Link up with a display of "FIT-BITS" and increase your sales.

FROG MODEL AIRCRAFT.

Note the new models "Avenger" retailing at 1/- and 1/11d. and "Raider" retailing at 1/11d. and 2/11d.

The FROG "PENGUIN" range of non-flying scale-model construction kits has been greatly increased. These models when finished are replicas in miniature of well-known types of Civil and Military Aircraft.

TERMS. The retail prices which appear in RED are the maintained selling prices, and our goods are sold on the understanding that these prices are strictly adhered to. The wholesale prices shown in BLACK type are subject to 50% Discount. PLEASE CAREFULLY EXAMINE NEW PRICE-LIST BEFORE MARKING UP PRICES.

CASH DISCOUNT. We allow 2½% discount for cash received on or before the 20th of the month following that in which the goods are invoiced.

CARRIAGE. We pay on consignments of £10 or more, if sent to one address.

We thank you for your valued orders in the past and look forward to your continued favours.

Yours faithfully,
LINES BROS. LTD.

Tri-ang
TOYS

The Perfect Model!

L.B.4242

LINES BROS. LTD.

LIST No. 39 1937/38
COPYRIGHT.
FROG MODEL AIRCRAFT
ILLUSTRATED AND DESCRIBED IN
SECTIONAL CATALOGUE No. 39a

Birmingham Branch:
UNIQUE AND UNITY
CYCLE Co., Ltd.
(Proprietors:
Lines Bros., Ltd.)
Extensive New Works
Camp Lane, Handsworth,
Birmingham, 21

Telephone:
Aston Cross 3588-9

Lines Bros Ltd

DIRECTORS : W. J. LINES, WALTER LINES, A. E. LINES, G. M. CAMPBELL, R. C. MUNRO, R. FREEMAN, G. F. R. BAGULEY.

MANUFACTURERS & EXPORTERS
OF NOVEL & BEST FINISHED TOYS
HEAD OFFICE & WORKS & ALL LETTERS TO

Head Office & Works.
Telephone:
LIBerty 4242 (6 lines)
60 Extensions to all
departments

Telegrams:
Triangtois, Phone,
London

Code:
Western Union (5 letter)

TRI-ANG WORKS, MORDEN ROAD, MERTON, LONDON, S.W.19, ENGLAND
Spacious City Showrooms : 18 NEW UNION ST., LONDON, E.C.2   Telephone : METropolitan 0337

A CORDIAL invitation to visit Tri-ang Works is open to you at all times. Occupying a large site, of which over 15 acres are covered by the factory buildings. Tri-ang Works are equipped with up-to-date plant and machinery that ensures high-class economic production. The tremendous amount of work entailed in the manufacture of Tri-ang toys must be seen to be appreciated. We shall be pleased to show you round, as we feel that a more intimate knowledge of the goods you are handling must be of considerable help.

LINES BROS. reserve the right to vary the design, construction and prices of any of these toys without notice. Dimensions throughout are approximate, but care has been taken to get them as accurate as possible. Measurements have been taken "overall."

LINES BROS.' goods are supplied on the distinct understanding that those articles specially marked in red ink in the price key with the retail selling price must be sold to the public at this full price, and that no extras are to be included without adequate proportional extra charge to the customer.

EXPORT Trade is specially catered for. The packing of most of our toys in fibreboard cartons was the result of many years' keen study of Export conditions and problems, thus reducing freight costs to a minimum and allowing us to offer Tri-ang Toys to Traders Overseas at very KEEN PRICES.

SCIENTIFIC PACKING

LINES BROS.' introduction of the Carton system of packing for large toys has entailed very heavy expense, but this has been amply justified by the satisfaction given to our customers.

It has saved them the major proportion of loss by deterioration of stock, also a considerable percentage of their packing and handling costs.

Export customers will appreciate the fact that the smallest size box possible is used in every case and that they are easily packed in crates or cases to take up very little room.

EXPORT.—The advantages of this system are obvious. In some cases goods are knocked down and boxes still further reduced in size.

ORDERING

To avoid possibility of error, please quote reference number of all goods, in addition to name and size.

L.B. Ltd
FIBREBOARD BOXES

HOW TO GET
TO OUR WORKS

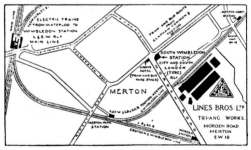

Edgware-Morden Line Underground to South Wimbledon Station (top of Morden Road). By means of this Tube and its connections, it is easy to reach our Works in about half-an-hour from any part of London. From Wimbledon Main Line Station (Southern Railway) it is five minutes by 'Bus to the entrance of our Works.

SPECIAL NOTE
Tri-ang Mickey Mouse Toys and Nursery Furniture are only available for export to countries in the British Empire.

We have Agents in the following Countries :

ARGENTINE	HOLLAND
ARABIA	ICELAND
AUSTRALIA	INDIA
BELGIUM	JAMAICA
BRAZIL	LITHUANIA
BRITISH W. INDIES	MALTA
CANADA	NEW ZEALAND
CANARY ISLANDS	NORWAY
CHINA	PALESTINE
COLUMBIA, S.A.	PERU
CYPRUS	PORTUGAL
DENMARK	S. AFRICA
DUTCH E. INDIES	STRAITS
E. AFRICA	SETTLEMENTS
EGYPT	SYRIA
FINLAND	SWEDEN
FRANCE	TURKEY W. AFRICA

THE HOME OF TRI-ANG TOYS
The Largest Toy Factory in the World

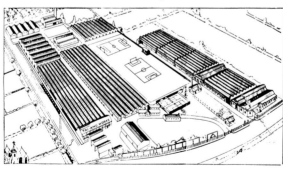

THE UNIQUE & UNITY CYCLE CO., LTD.,
Props: LINES BROS., LTD.
MAKERS OF THE WORLD FAMOUS FAIRYCYCLE AND TRI-ANG TRICYCLES
Regd. Trade Mark

We have pleasure in announcing to the Trade that our new cycle factory, covering over two acres is now in full production.
We are confident that our friends in the Trade will find that the products of the Unique & Unity Cycle Co., always renowned for highest quality and lowest prices, will continue to set the highest standard of value.
In order to ensure this, the finest plant has been installed in every department. It can safely be said that no cycle factory has better equipment.

FROG MODEL AIRCRAFT is illustrated and described in Sectional Catalogue 39A.

LOW PRICED, STRONGLY CONSTRUCTED
CARS WITH DOUBLE CRANK DRIVE

TRI-ANG CROWN

2646

All steel body, pressed radiator, 6" direct spoke wheels, $\frac{7}{16}$" grey rubber tyres. Appearance has been greatly improved, the tracking bar is now inside the radiator and the body is lower on the axles. Length $26\frac{1}{4}$". Ages 2 to 4.

TRI-ANG PRINCE

2647

All steel body, bright metal radiator, realistic louvres, 6" disc wheels, $\frac{1}{2}$" rubber tyres. A strongly constructed motor for the small child. Length 29". Ages 2 to 4.

TRI-ANG JUBILEE

2648

A new model, very strongly constructed. All steel body, bright radiator, realistic louvres, 6" tangent spoke wheels, $\frac{5}{8}$" tyres. Two dummy lamps and rimless windscreen. Length $29\frac{1}{2}$". Ages 2 to 4.

TRI-ANG BENTLEY JUNIOR

2649

Pressed steel body, with opening side door. Model Bentley radiator, 6" steel disc wheels, $\frac{1}{2}$" rubber tyres, petrol and oil cans. Length 30". For ages 2 to 4.

TRI-ANG BENTLEY TOURER

(Not illustrated)

2649A

Pressed steel body with opening side door. Model Bentley radiator, 6" disc wheels, $\frac{1}{2}$" rubber tyres, windscreen with tubular frame, dummy hood realistically made from wood, two lamps, mudguards coloured to match body. Petrol and oil cans. For ages 2 to 4. Length 32".

Page One

L.B.Ltd
MITCHAM

TRI-ANG MITCHAM
2650

Pressed steel body, Magna type radiator with plated top and rim. Windscreen with tubular frame, dummy hood and lamps, 8" balloon disc wheels, ½" rubber tyres. Petrol and oil cans. Body and mudguards nicely finished in beige. Length 32½". Ages 2 to 4.

L.B.Ltd
VAUXHALL TOURER

TRI-ANG VAUXHALL TOURER
2651

Pressed steel body with opening side door and facsimile Vauxhall bonnet and radiator with plated flares, windscreen with tubular frame, dummy hood and lamps, 8" balloon disc wheels, ½" rubber tyres. Petrol and oil cans. Length 32½". Ages 2 to 4.

L.B.Ltd
TRI-ANG JUNIOR

TRI-ANG JUNIOR
2652

New design. Pressed steel body, opening side door, plated streamline radiator, windscreen and metal dummy hood. 8" balloon disc wheels, ½" rubber tyres. Petrol and oil cans. Length 34". Ages 2 to 4.

TRI-ANG VAUXHALL SPECIAL
2653

Pressed steel body with opening side door, facsimile Vauxhall bonnet and radiator with plated flares, windscreen with tubular frame, dummy hood and plated lamps, 8½" tangent spoke wheels, 1" jointless cushion tyres. Now fitted with pressed steel bumper (see Tri-ang Daimler, page 3). Petrol and oil cans. Length 34". Ages 2 to 4.

L.B.Ltd
VAUXHALL SPECIAL

TRI-ANG DAIMLER

2654

Modern design, pressed steel body with opening side door, **ball-bearing back axle,** adjustable windscreen and indicator, facsimile Daimler radiator, pressed bumper, dummy hood and lamps. 9″ balloon disc wheels, ⅝″ rubber tyres. Length 37¼″. Ages 3 to 6.

L.B.Ltd
TRI-ANG DAIMLER

TRI-ANG SPORTS

2655

A realistic streamlined model with the latest type radiator and domed mudguards. Steel body with opening side door and luggage boot, **ball-bearing back axle,** 8″ balloon disc wheels, large hub caps, ½″ rubber tyres, plated bumper and streamline dummy side lamps fitted to bonnet, windscreen, direction indicator, dummy hood and petrol and oil cans. Length 41″. For ages 4 to 6 years.

L.B.Ltd
TRI-ANG SPORTS

TRI-ANG PREMIER

2656

Magnificent new model. Pressed steel body, opening side door and luggage locker, 8″ balloon disc wheels, ½″ rubber tyres, **ball-bearing back axle,** latest type Vauxhall radiator. All bright parts **chromium plated,** including radiator, steering, windscreen, lamps and flares. Length 39″. Ages 3 to 6.

L.B.Ltd
TRI-ANG PREMIER

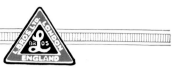

L.B.Ltd
TRI-ANG SPECIAL

TRI-ANG SPECIAL

2657

Entirely new and modern design, steel body with opening side door and luggage boot, latest type radiator with mascot, domed mudguards, **ball-bearing back axle**, 8″ tangent spoke wheels, 1″ jointless cushion tyres, chromium-plated steering, bumper and streamline dummy side lamps fitted to bonnet. Windscreen, direction indicator and dummy hood. Petrol and oil cans. Length 41″. For ages 4 to 6 years.

TRI-ANG EPOCH

2658

Very modern design, with opening side door and latest type radiator, **crank drive on ball-bearing back axle**, pressed steel bumper (see Tri-ang Major, below), adjustable windscreen with tubular frame, two latest type side lamps embodied on graceful wings, two head lamps. 9″ balloon wheels, with latest type Magna hub caps, ⅝″ rubber tyres. Adjustable seat. Length 43″. Suitable for ages 5 to 7.

L.B.Ltd
EPOCH

L.B.Ltd
TRIANG MAJOR

TRI-ANG MAJOR

2659

Entirely new design. Steel body with opening side door and adjustable seat, two electric side lamps embodied on the wings, plated streamline radiator, 8½″ diam. tangent spoke wheels, 10″ × 1 1/16″ Auto-tread tyres, **ball-bearing back axle**, adjustable windscreen and direction indicator, dummy hood. Length 43″. For ages 5 to 7.

L.B.Ltd
STREAMLINE

TRI-ANG STREAMLINE

2660

Latest type streamline model, body of pressed steel, with opening side door, **crank drive, ball-bearing back axle,** facsimile Airflow radiator with mascot, two sunken headlights, and dummy side, pressed steel bumpers back and front (see Tri-ang de Luxe below), adjustable windscreen with tubular frame. Direction indicator, adjustable seat, latest Chrysler type mudguards. 9″ balloon disc wheels, ⅝″ rubber tyres. Length 45″. Suitable for ages 5 to 7.

TRI-ANG DE LUXE

2661

A magnificent new model with aluminium body, opening side door and luggage boot, modern domed mudguards in contrasting colour, latest type radiator with mascot, chromium-plated streamline electric side lamps mounted on the bonnet, 8½″ tangent spoke wheels with Magna hubs, 1¼″ jointless sponge rubber tyres. **Ball-bearing back axle,** windscreen direction indicator and dummy hood. **All bright parts chromium-plated.** Length 41″. For ages 4 to 6.

L.B.Ltd
TRI-ANG DE LUXE

TRI-ANG SCEPTRE

2662

Latest design sports body. **Chain and crank drive, tubular chassis, and windscreen,** pressed steel bumpers (see Tri-ang de Luxe above), dummy hood, opening side door, modern type radiator, two latest type electric side lamps embodied on wings, electric stop and go sign and Klakker horn ; adjustable seat. Two head lamps. 8½″ diameter tangent spoke wheels with latest type Magna hubs cap, 10″×1⅛″ jointless sponge rubber tyres. **Chromium-plated hubs and rims.** Ages 5 to 7.

L.B.Ltd
SCEPTRE

TRI-ANG
PEDAL LOCO
AND
PEDAL PLANES,
ETC.

TRI-ANG PEDAL LOCO

2679

Modelled on style of L.M.S. engines, and fitted with 9″ steel disc balloon wheels, with ⅝″ grey rubber tyres. Seat upholstered, rubber pedals, whistle included. Double crank drive. Painted bright red, neatly lined out. One lamp. Fitted with new type Magna hub caps. Length 42¾″.

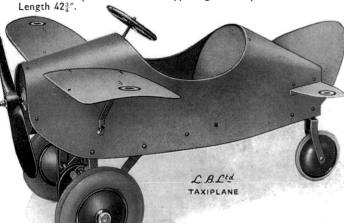

TAXIPLANE

TRI-ANG
TAXI MONOPLANE

2680

An inexpensive one-seater model with revolving propeller. Fuselage of light sheet steel. Upholstered seat in cockpit. Steering from rear wheel. Pedal driven, balloon disc wheels, rubber tyres. Wings detach to save space. Fitted with new type Magna hub caps. Length 42½″.

TRI-ANG
IMPERIAL AIRWAYS

No. 2   2683

Modelled after the big air liners now in use. The nickel-plated propellers revolve when 'plane is pulled along, and at the same time a ratchet produces the sound of the engine. Steel wheels, rubber tyres. Strongly made of steel, highly finished.

IMPERIAL AIRWAYS No. 1   2682
(Not illustrated)

Exactly as above, but with one dummy engine and rotating propeller. Length 24½″.

IMPERIAL AIRWAYS No. 2.

TRANSATLANTIC

TRI-ANG
TRANSATLANTIC PLANE

2681

Much improved design with polished aluminium body, upholstered seats in cockpit, balloon disc wheels, rubber tyres. Revolving polished walnut propeller and dummy rotary engine. Steering from rear disc wheel. Rubber pedals. The wings detach and the tailplanes fold to save space. Fitted with new type Magna hub caps. Length 54″.

DOLLS' PRAMS

2690

18/A. Moulded sides, 6″ wheels with ½″ tyres, leather cloth hood and apron, nickel-plated folding handles, and joints on hood. Length of body 18″.

2688

16/A. (Not illustrated.) Similar specification to 18/A, but smaller body and 5″ wheels.

2685

16/S. (Illustrated.) Steel body, length 16″, with attractive moulding. Improved hood with plated joints. Folding handle. 5″ wheels, ⅜″ tyres.

2684

14/S. (Not illustrated.) 14″ body with pleasing moulded design.

2686

18/S. (Not illustrated.) 18″ body with moulded design.

2687

20/S. (Not illustrated.) 20″ body with moulded design.

2693

20/B. Outside springs, 6″ tangent spoke wheels, ⅝″ white tyres, laced hood, two pairs mudguards, black levers, leather cloth hood and apron. Length of body 20″.

2689

16/UT. Moulded body, 5″ wheels, ½″ tyres, black levers, leather cloth hood and apron, nickel-plated joints. Length of body 16″.

2692

18/UT. Moulded steel body, with pleasing design folding black handles, four mudguards, leather cloth hood and apron and nickel-plated joints, 6″ wheels and ½″ tyres. Length of body 18″.

2691

18/B. Moulded sides, outside springs, four mudguards, 6″ wheels, ½″ tyres, leather cloth hood and apron, laced hood, nickel-plated joints. Nickel-plated folding handles. Length of body 18″.

2694

20/W. New style boat-shape body outside springs, 6″ tangent spoke wheels, ⅝″ white tyres, nicely upholstered, laced hood, apron, long black levers, toy waist strap, two pairs dressguards and footbrake. Length of body 20″.

2695

22/W. Attractive boat-shape body. Outside springs, 6″ tangent spoke wheels, ⅝″ white tyres, nicely upholstered with laced hood, and 9″ tubular joints. Apron with storm flap. Toy waist strap, long black levers. Two pairs dressguards and footbrake. Length of body 22″.

DOLLS' PRAMS

2698

24/O. Stylish new boatshape with attractive design. Leather cloth lined hood and apron, hood is also laced. 7″ tangent spoke wheels, ⅝″ tyres, one pair dressguards, new strapless outside springs. Length of body 24″.

2697

22/UT. Steel body with attractive design moulded on panels, black levers with white rubber grip, 6″ tangent spoke wheels, 1″ cushion tyres, two pairs mudguards, laced hood, storm flap to apron. Length of body 22″.

2696

22/B. Attractive moulded design, 7″ tangent spoke wheels with 1″ cushion tyres, leather cloth hood lined and laced, apron and storm flap, four dressguards, plated hood joints. Footbrake now fitted. Length of body 22″.

2699

24/W. Boatshape body of pleasing design, well upholstered, leather cloth hood with lace, long black tubular levers, outside strap hung springs, 7″ tangent spoke wheels, ⅝″ white tyres. Two pairs dressguards and footbrake. Length of body 24″.

2700

24/S. An attractive boatshape body, well upholstered. Leather cloth hood with lace, chromium-plated joints, outside springs, 7″ tangent spoke wheels, 1″ cushion tyres. two pairs dressguards and footbrake, **All bright parts,** including long levers and wheel rims, **chromium-plated.** Length of body 24″

2698

Page Twelve

DOLLS' PRAMS

2702

24/D. The body is nicely upholstered, with piped arms and back, and the hood is leather cloth and laced, 7" tangent spoke wheels, 1" cushion tyres, two pairs dressguards, footbrake, and all bright parts, including hood joints, levers and rims, are chromium-plated. Length of body 24".

2703

24/K. A handsome design with steel body neatly moulded and lined, non-tracking tangent spoke wheels, 10" × 1" jointless cushion tyres, outside strap-hung springs, leather cloth hood (lined and laced) and apron with storm flap, piped arms and back. Chromium-plated handles, also rims of wheels. Length of body 24".

2704

26/K. (Not illustrated.) Similar specification to 24/K but with 26" body and 12" × 1" jointless cushion tyres.

2705

26/W. New design boatshape body, well upholstered, with leather cloth hood and apron, long stove enamelled levers. 7" tangent spoke wheels, 1" cushion tyres, two pairs dressguards and latest type footbrake. Length of body 26".

2701

24/X. A stylish design. Steel body, nicely upholstered, with leather cloth hood and apron, the hood is laced and has new style joints and the apron has a storm flap, 7" tangent spoke wheels, 1" cushion tyres, latest type footbrake and two pairs dressguards. Length of body 24".

2706

ADVANCE. The latest streamline design. Well upholstered, leather cloth hood and apron, chromium-plated pump handle joints. 7" tangent spoke wheels, 1" cushion tyres. Chromium-plated rims and folding handles with rubber grip. Length of body overall 28", and 22½" × 10" on top.

DOLLS' PRAMS

2707

26/C. A very attractive new boatshape body, nicely upholstered, with piped arms and back and loose cushion seats. Leather cloth hood and apron. 7" tangent spoke wheels, 1" cushion tyres, two pairs dressguards and footbrake. All bright parts, including long levers, wheel rims and hood joints, **chromium-plated.** Length of body 26".

2709

26/TC. A magnificent Doll's Pram. Stylish boatshape body, well upholstered, with piped arms and back and loose cushion seats. The body is suspended by four chromium-plated coil springs on to the chromium-plated chassis, which is best quality tapered steel tubing. 8½" non-track tangent spoke wheels, 1" cushion tyres, one pair dressguards and footbrake. All bright parts, including long levers, wheel rims and hood joints, are **chromium-plated.** Length of body 26".

2708

26/T. Similar specification to 26/TC, but stove enamelled levers and tubular chassis.

DOLLS' BED FOLDERS

2711

5/DBF. Fully enclosed bed with adjustable drop end, hood laced and apron fitted with storm flap. Stove enamelled tubular chassis on four coil springs, 6" tangent spoke wheels, ⅝" tyres. Stove enamelled reversible levers, with rubber grip. Length of body 24".

2712

6/DBF. A scale model of a full sized Pedigree Folder. Fully enclosed bed with adjustable drop end, hood laced and apron fitted with storm flap. Chromium-plated tubular chassis on four coil springs, 6" tangent-spoke wheels, 1" cushion tyres. Two pairs dressguards. All bright parts, including hood joints, rims and reversible levers, chromium-plated. Length of body 24".

2710

1/DBF. New model with easy-action folding frame. Hood lined, laced and fitted with chromium-plated pump joints. Apron fitted with storm flap. Stove enamelled reversible levers with rubber grip. Chassis on four coil springs, 6" tangent spoke wheels, 1" cushion tyres. Length of body 23".

 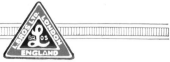

2713

00/DBF. Complete folding movement, one-piece tubular handle, 5″ direct spoke wheels with ½″ white rubber tyres, black stove-enamelled frame.

2715

D. GIANT. Easy action folding. Fully enclosed bed, with lift-up front. Hood and apron, reversible handles with rubber grip, 6″ tangent spoke wheels, ⅝″ tyres and two coil springs on rear axle.

2714

0/DBF. Four coil spring chassis with 6″ wheels and ½″ white rubber tyres, black tubular handles. Tubular hood joints.

2716

0/SUNKAR. Reversible backrest, upholstered seat and back, folding levers, 5″ direct spoke wheels, ⅜″ rubber tyres.

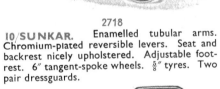

2718

10/SUNKAR. Enamelled tubular arms. Chromium-plated reversible levers. Seat and backrest nicely upholstered. Adjustable footrest. 6″ tangent-spoke wheels. ⅝″ tyres. Two pair dressguards.

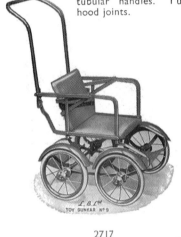

2717

9/SUNKAR. Reversible backrest. Nicely upholstered seat and back, safety strap. 6″ tangent-spoke wheels, ⅝″ tyres. Two pair dressguards.

2719

DOT. Light and strong, stove enamelled frame, 2″ steel disc wheels and rubber tyres. Tubular handle, leather cloth seat. Excellent value.

2720

MIDGET 3″ steel disc wheels, rubber tyres. Steel frame, stove-enamelled. Tubular handle, lift-up front.

2721

ELF. Folding frame, lift-up footrest, tubular handle, 5″ spoke wheels, ⅜″ rubber tyres. Stove enamelled. Splendid value.

2722

"A" GIANT FOLDER. Full tubular handle, wood seat covered leather cloth. 5″ spoke wheels, ⅜″ rubber tyres. Just like full-size folders.

PEDAL KARS

No. 0 PEDALKAR
2723

New model, very strongly constructed, steel disc wheels, rubber tyres, steel seat and handlebars with rubber grip.

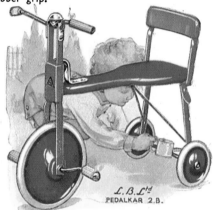

No. 40A SAFETY PEDALKAR
2732

Now fitted with a cycle bell. Improved seat with shaped back-rest, finished pale green enamel. White tyres on red steel disc wheels. Plated handlebars. Rubber grips and pedals.

No. 1 PEDALKAR
2724

All steel construction, disc wheels with white tyres, rubber pedals and handle grips. Mickey Mouse transfer on seat. Folds flat. Packed four in a box.

2725
No. 1B. Similar to No. 1, but larger overall dimensions. Packed two in a box.

No. 2/B PEDALKAR
2726

Now fitted with a bell. All steel construction, takes apart to fit in box. Steel wheels, $\frac{1}{2}''$ rubber tyres. Rubber pedals and handle grips, safety back-rest. Enamelled red and blue. Nickel-plated cranks.

No. 4A PEDALKAR
2727

Now fitted with a bell. Pressed steel seat and back-rest. Steel disc wheels, $\frac{1}{2}''$ rubber tyres. Nickel-plated handlebars, rubber grips and pedals.

2728
No. 4S. As 4A, but with $\frac{3}{4}''$ white auto-tread tyres.

No. 4B PEDALKAR
2729

Now fitted with a bell. Pressed steel seat and back-rest. 8″ steel balloon disc wheels, $\frac{5}{8}''$ rubber tyres. Nickel-plated handle-bars, rubber grips and pedals.

No. 4SS PEDALKAR
2730

Now fitted with cycle bell. Popular model, finished red and blue with nickel-plated handlebars and cranks. 7″ tangent spoke wheels fitted with $1\frac{1}{8}''$ white jointless sponge rubber tyres.

No. 4XX PEDALKAR
2731

A de luxe model, similar to 4SS, but with chromium-plated handlebars, forks, cranks, back-rest, and hubs and rims.

PEDALKARS
AND
NURSERY TOYS

5B PEDALKAR

2733

Now fitted with cycle bell. A large model with steel balloon wheels, front ball-bearing. Nickel-plated tubular handles, improved back-rest. Finished red and blue. Height to seat 13½".

2734

No. 5XX. **SPECIAL ALL CHROM.** Chromium-plated handlebars, forks, cranks, and stays to back-rest.

PEDALKAR 7.

2735

Now fitted with cycle bell. Wooden seat and back-rest, stained and polished. Nickel-plated handlebars and cranks with rubber pedals and handlebar grips. Tangent spoke wheels, fitted with white tyres. A very strong and durable model. Height to seat 13½".

GEE GEE KAR

2736

A nursery toy with realistic horse's head. Tray with coloured castor beads. Runs easily on 3" rubber-tyred castors. Rubber buffers fitted. Finished washable red enamel.

DOBBIN HAND CAR

2737

A new and novel Chariot Racer. Crank drive. Steel disc wheels, with rubber tyres. Nicely finished in colours.

GUARDSMAN TODDLEKAR

2738

Novel new design. Very strongly constructed, with low centre of gravity. Fitted with 2" rubber-tyred castors. Guardsman attractively coloured. Transfer and beads on play-tray.

Page Seventeen

TODDLEKARS

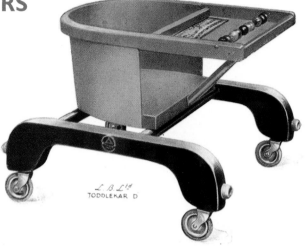

TODDLEKAR "B"

2739

Coloured beads and transfer on tray. Rubber buffers and wheels. Seat 5½" from ground. Finished blue or pink.

TODDLEKAR "D"
(Junior)

2740

Stoutly constructed with low centre of gravity, making it impossible to overturn. Finished blue washable enamel, with coloured beads. Castors with 2" rubber-tyred wheels. Rubber buffers back and front. Packed each in a box.

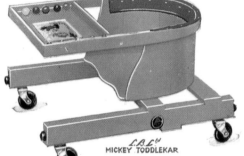

MICKEY TODDLEKAR

2741

New model with upholstered back. Mickey transfer and beads on play-tray. Rubber buffers back and front. Runs smoothly on rubber wheels.

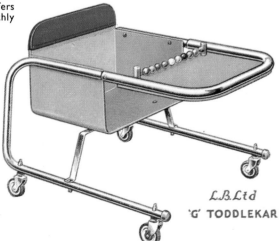

TODDLEKAR "E" (Senior)

2742

Finished washable tango enamel, mounted on 3" rubber-tyred castors. Rubber buffers back and front. Easy to push, even over a deep pile carpet. Very low centre of gravity. Tray has coloured beads and educational transfer showing numerals, letters and animals. Detchable foot-rest included.

TODDLEKAR "G"
NOW HAS PADDED ARM RESTS

2743

Improved model with a chromium-plated tubular frame and padded arm rests. Tray with coloured beads, 2" rubber-tyred castors. Padded back-rest. Nicely finished in cellulose enamel.

 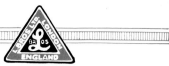

SCOOTERS

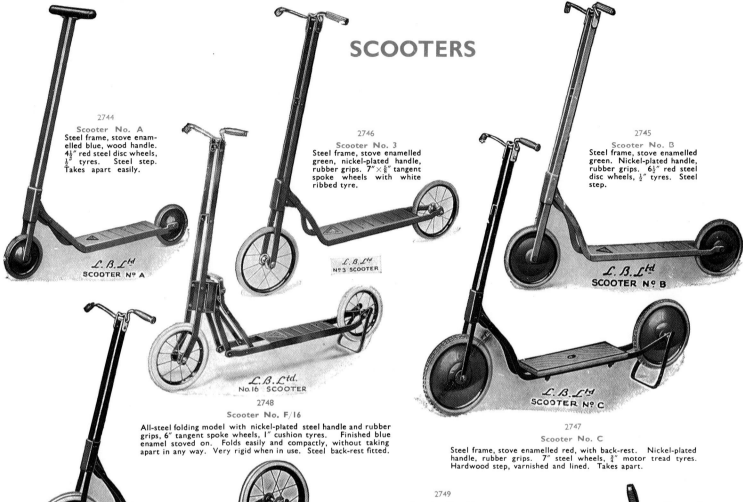

2744
Scooter No. A
Steel frame, stove enamelled blue, wood handle. 4½" red steel disc wheels, 1½" tyres. Steel step. Takes apart easily.

2746
Scooter No. 3
Steel frame, stove enamelled green, nickel-plated handle, rubber grips. 7" × ⅝" tangent spoke wheels with white ribbed tyre.

2745
Scooter No. B
Steel frame, stove enamelled green. Nickel-plated handle, rubber grips. 6½" red steel disc wheels, ½" tyres. Steel step.

2748
Scooter No. F/16
All-steel folding model with nickel-plated steel handle and rubber grips, 6" tangent spoke wheels, 1" cushion tyres. Finished blue enamel stoved on. Folds easily and compactly, without taking apart in any way. Very rigid when in use. Steel back-rest fitted.

2747
Scooter No. C
Steel frame, stove enamelled red, with back-rest. Nickel-plated handle, rubber grips. 7" steel wheels, ¾" motor tread tyres. Hardwood step, varnished and lined. Takes apart.

2749
Scooter No. D
Strong steel frame, stove enamelled red, with back-rest. Nickel-plated handle, rubber grips. Tangent spoke wheels, 10" × 1" cushion tyres, 8½" diameter rims. BAND BRAKE ON REAR WHEEL. Hardwood step, varnished and lined. Takes apart.

2750
No. F. As D, but with ball-bearing wheels, plated hubs, cushion tyres.

2751
No. G. As F, but chromium-plated hubs, rims and handles. Ball-bearing wheels.

Tri-ang Scoot No. F/20. 2754
A luxury model with 12½" tangent spoke wheels and 2¼" Dunlop cord balloon pneumatic tyres. Special cycle type tubular handlebars fitted with rim brake. Wood board with foot mat. Enamelled blue. Chromium-plated fittings.

Tri-ang Scoot No. F/20C. 2755
Special all chromium, including frame, rims and hubs, etc.

Tri-ang Scoot No. F/8. 2752
Frame constructed with the best weldless steel cycle tubing, and fitted with 10" tangent spoke ball-bearing wheels and 1" cushion rubber tyres. Plunger spoon pattern brake on the front tyre. Ample width footboard. Raised pattern handlebars, with black grips. Enamelled blue. Chromium-plated fittings.

Tri-ang Scoot No. F/8C. 2753
Special all chromium, including frame, rims and hubs, etc.

STILTS 2756.
Beautifully finished in blue, these metal stilts are fitted with rubber pads and adjustable rubber footrests. Height 5 ft.

Tri-ang Toys
The mark of Perfection

The Fairycycle

REGD TRADE MARK

We remind the trade that the word "Fairycycle" is Lines Bros.' Registered Trade Mark. Legal proceedings will be taken against anyone selling, advertising, offering or exposing for sale any cycle or similar goods not being the manufacture of Lines Bros., Ltd., under the name of "FAIRYCYCLE" or under any name imitated therefrom or liable to be mistaken therefor.

L.B.Lᵗᵈ FAIRYCYCLE (REGᴰ TRADE MARK) **MODEL Nº 2**

FAIRYCYCLE (Regd.) **Model 2.** 2758

Tubular frame. 14″ wheels. 1⅜″ auto-tread tyres. Ball-bearing pedals. Rim brake. Two-coil saddle. Chain cover stand. Black, blue or maroon. **Chromium-Plated Fittings.**

L.B.Lᵗᵈ TRI-ANG CYCLE Nº O

TRI-ANG CYCLE No. 0.
2757

Tubular frame. 13″ wheels, 1″ cushion tyres. Spoon brake. Free-wheel. Frame enamelled black, blue, or maroon. **Chromium-Plated** handlebars. Cover to chain.

L.B.Lᵗᵈ FAIRYCYCLE (REGᴰ TRADE MARK) **MODEL Nº 3.**

FAIRYCYCLE (Regd.) **Model 3.**
2759

Ball-bearing wheels, pedals and bracket. 14″ wheels, 1⅜″ sponge tyres. Rim brake. Two coil leather saddle. Chain cover, stand. Reflector. Black, blue or maroon. **Chromium-Plated Fittings.**

L.B.Lᵗᵈ FAIRYCYCLE (REGᴰ TRADE MARK) **MODEL Nº 4**

FAIRYCYCLE (Regd.) **Model 4.** 2760

Dunlop pneumatic tyres. Ball-bearing wheels and pedals. 14″ × 1⅜″ wheels. Rim brake. Chain cover, stand. Black, blue, or maroon. **Chromium-Plated Fittings.**

FAIRYCYCLE (Regd.) **Model 6.** 2761

Larger model with 16″ wheels, 1½″ Dunlop solid tyres. Ball-bearings throughout. Rim brake. Two coil saddle. Black, blue, or maroon. **Chromium-Plated Fittings.**

L.B.Lᵗᵈ FAIRYCYCLE (REGᴰ TRADE MARK) **MODEL Nº 6**

TRI-ANG CARRIER TRICYCLES

L.B.Lᵗᵈ Nº 3 TRI-ANG TIP CARRIER TRICYCLE

No. 3 TRI-ANG TIP CARRIER TRICYCLE. 2763

Strongly made of best weldless steel cycle tubing. Ball-bearings throughout. Leather saddle. Tangent spoke wheels. Jointless sponge tyres. Box at rear and special tipping gear. Fitted with bell, electric front and rear lamps. **Chromium-Plated** handlebars, forks, etc. Box finished red. Frame blue.

L.B.Lᵗᵈ TOT TRIKE CARRIER

TOT CARRIER TRIKE. 2762

Red stove enamelled frame. 14″ front wheel. 1⅜″ motor tread tyres. 9½″ rear wheels. ¾″ motor tread tyres. Fitted with rear mudguards. Steel box finished red and grey. Useful for carrying parcels and other articles. Very strong construction.

Page Twenty

TRI-ANG "UNITY" JUVENILE CYCLES

" UNITY " CYCLES 16 & 18 SB (Boys'), 16 & 18 SG (Girls') 2764
For Boys and Girls. 16″ and 18″ frames. Finest quality British steel tube frame. Wheels 16″×1⅜″ for 16″ frames and 18″×1⅜″ for 18″ frames. Dunlop cushion tyres. Rim brake to front wheel. Two coil leather saddle. Ball-bearing pedals. Finish, black, blue, or maroon. Usual bright parts **Chromium-plated.**

" UNITY " CYCLE No. 16 PB (Boys') 2765
16″ frame of best quality weldless steel cycle tubing. Adjustable ball-bearings throughout. 16″×1⅜″ Dunlop pneumatic tyres on rustless tangent spoked wheels. Two rim brakes. Raised handlebars. ½″×⅛″ cycle roller chain. Three-coil saddle. Black, blue, or maroon. **Chromium-plated Fittings.** For ages 6 to 10.

" UNITY " JUVENILE CYCLE No. 16 FG (Girls') 2766
Similar specification to 16 BP, but with open frame.

" UNITY " BOYS' CYCLE No. 18 PB 2767
18″ frame. Finest quality British tube. Wheels 18″×1⅜″, **Chromium-plated** rims, Dunlop pneumatic tyres. Roller lever pattern brakes, Three-coil saddle, ½″×⅛″ roller chain. Ball-bearings throughout. Complete with equipment and finished in black or blue. All usual bright parts **Chromium-plated.** Ages 7 to 11.

" UNITY " BOYS' JUVENILE CYCLE No. 20 PB 2769
Similar to No. 18 PB, but wheels 20″×1⅜″. Dunlop pneumatic tyres, and Wright's super-sprung saddle. Suitable for ages 8 to 12.

" UNITY " GIRLS' CYCLE No. 18 PG 2768
18″ open pattern frame, made from finest quality British tube. Wheels 18″×1⅜″, **Chromium-plated** rims. Dunlop tyres, roller lever pattern brakes, three-coil saddle, ½″×⅛″ roller chain. Ball-bearings throughout. Complete with equipment and finished in black or blue. All usual bright parts **Chromium-plated.** Ages 7 to 11.

" UNITY " GIRLS' JUVENILE CYCLE No. 20 PG 2770
Similar to No. 18 PG, but with 20″×1⅜″ Dunlop pneumatic tyres, and Wright's super-sprung saddle. Suitable for ages 8 to 12.

18/24 AND 20/26 " UNITY " BOYS' " POPULAR " MODELS 2771
18″ or 20″ frames, built with finest quality British steel. 24″ and 26″ wheels. Dunlop Champion tyres. Chain, Perry ½″×⅛″. Good quality leather saddle. Ball-bearings throughout. Complete with equipment and finished in finest black enamel, lined in green and gold. Usual bright parts **Chromium-plated.**

18/24 AND 20/26 " UNITY " GIRLS' " POPULAR " MODELS 2772
(Not illustrated.) Same specification as above, but with open frame.
18/24 has 18 in. frame and 24 in. wheels.
20/26 „ 20 in. „ „ 26 in. „

L.B.Ltd
METAL TIPPING LORRY I/T

L.B.Ltd
METAL VAN I/V

L.B.Ltd
BREAKDOWN LORRY I/BL

METAL TIPPING LORRY I T
2792
Designed on the same lines as the real thing. Body-tipping is operated by lever from the driving cab. Steel disc wheels, rubber tyres. Length 18″.

METAL VAN I/V
2793
An attractive toy, soundly built of steel on engineering principles. Adjustable tail-board. Now has R.M. plates on both sides. Steel disc wheels, rubber tyres. Length 17¼″.

METAL BREAKDOWN LORRY I/BL
2794
Almost unbreakable, constructed of heavy gauge sheet steel. Working model crane swivels on chassis, chain winding gear controlled by non-slip ratchet, adjustable jib and loading block. Steel disc wheels, rubber tyres. Length 15¼″.

L.B.Ltd
L.C.C. FIRE ENGINE

WOOD L.C.C. FIRE ENGINE
2796
Realistic toy, modelled on the lines of the latest type L.C.C. Fire Engines. Nicely coloured and fitted with disc wheels and rubber tyres, ladder, hose and bell. Length 18″.

L.B.Ltd
WOOD MECHANICAL HORSE & WAGON

WOOD MECHANICAL HORSE AND WAGON
2795
New toy, strongly constructed and fitted with steel disc wheels and rubber tyres. Wagon is detachable. Nicely finished in red and yellow. Length 21½″.

L.B.L.
BUS No 2

L.B.L.
E.BUS

LONDON TRANSPORT OMNIBUS No. 2
2798
A realistic model of the latest 6-wheeler buses with inside staircase. Red steel disc wheels with rubber tyres. Domed mudguards. Fitted for one electric light, less battery. Length 29½″.

LONDON TRANSPORT OMNIBUS No. E   2797
Modelled on lines of latest double-deckers, four steel wheels with balloon rubber tyres. Fitted for one electric light, less battery. Inside staircase. Length 20¼″.

NON-MECHANICAL STEEL TOYS

CONSTRUCTION

Made of steel with strong axles and solid rubber wheels. Finished in brightly coloured enamel, immensely strong and almost indestructible.

PACKING

Sizes 0 and 00 are packed one in a carton (printed in colours) which are then packed in a fibreboard container. Sizes 000 are packed six in a box and 24 boxes in a strong fibreboard container.

ELECTRIC LIGHT

In most cases sizes 0 and 00 are obtainable fitted with electric light. Batteries of the cartridge type are **not** included. Models with electric light are specified as "OE" or "OOE."

BREAKDOWN LORRIES 2799

Rotating jib on each size. Chain and pulley wheel on sizes 0 and 00. Self-locking crank on each size. OE with two electric lights. OOE with one electric light.

FARM TRUCKS 2800

Popular series of general purpose motor truck. Three sizes: 0, 00 and 000. Also made as OE with two electric lights and OOE one electric light.

TIPPING LORRIES 2801

Well-known types of motor tipping lorries. Three sizes: 0, 00 and 000. Also made as OE with two electric lights and OOE with one electric light.

COUPÉ 2802

Attractive design of modern medium h.p. car. Nicely embossed, with louvres, etc.

OOE. As OO, but with one electric light.

FORWARD DRIVE LORRY 2803

Models of modern commercial motor vehicles. Nicely embossed, with radiator, lamps, etc. Large capacity body.

OE and OOE are fitted with one electric light.

RACING CARS 2804

Realistic model of track-racer. Streamlined body and tail. Radiator, louvres and exhaust manifold, embossed. OO fitted with spare wheel.

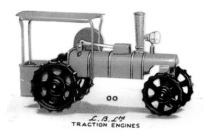

TRACTION ENGINES

TRACTION ENGINES 2805

Of similar construction to the steam rollers, but fitted with black rubber traction wheels.

OOE with one electric light (as illustrated).

OE with one electric light.

WAGON AND HORSES 2807

Each size has two steel horses, front bogie wheels and driver. A durable and novel toy.

STEAM ROLLERS

STEAM ROLLERS 2806

Sturdy construction and realistic appearance. Solid wooden drivers and front roller. Moving crank and dummy cylinder on O and OO sizes. Rotating flywheel.

OOE with one electric light (as illustrated).

OE with one electric light.

ROYAL MAIL VANS 2809

Nicely made, with attractively printed metal plates on sides. Tailboard lets down.

OE As O, but with two electric lights.

OOE (illustrated). As OO, but with one electric light.

L. B. Ltd.
OOO
VAN

VAN 2808

Popular design. Very strong. Tailboard lowers.

L. B. Ltd. **OOO**

GREEN LINE COACH 2810

Design based on well-known London motor coaches. Realistically embossed.

MONOPLANE 2811

A popular model of a high-wing monoplane. Fitted solid rubber wheels and revolving propeller.

TRI-ANG SWEEPER 2812

Faithful reproduction of modern suction sweeper. Fitted with revolving brush, dummy motor housing and black dust bag.

CRANES

L.B.L^td OO CRANE

L B L^td OOO CRANE

2814   2813

L.B.L^td OO/DOCK CRANE

L B L^td O/DOCK CRANE

CRANES SERIES OO and OOO

Realistic designs, all steel construction. Solid rubber wheels. Rotatory cab. Ratchet bar. Jib folds inside cab.
Size 000. Packed 6 in a box.

Height size 000. 4⅝″.
      „   „   00. 6¼″.

2816   2815

DOCK CRANES. SERIES O and OO

Similar construction to cranes OO and OOO, but on elevated legs which can be folded round cab to occupy minimum space. Sizes when folded : 7⅜″×7½″×6″ and 5½″×5⅞″×5″. Height of 00 9½″ ; 0 12⅝″.

2817

No. 1 CRANE

Height 8½″

2818

No. 2 CRANE

Height 10½″

CRANES

SERIES 1, 2 and 3

Stove enamelled red. No. 3 has black under-carriage. Joints welded together, practically unbreakable. Nos. 1 and 2 fitted with steel wheels. No. 3 has rubber tyres. Jibs fold down to save space when packing. Packed one in a box, and in the case of size No. 1, 24 boxes in a fibreboard case, measuring 26¾″ × 22½″ × 18″.

L.B.L^td CRANES

2819

No. 3 CRANE

L.B.L^td DOCK CRANE

2820

DOCK CRANE

All steel, on four steel wheels. Working model crane with chain winding gear. Crane swivels on stand. Very strong and well finished. Measurements given with jib folded.   Height 17¾″.

MINIC ALL TO SCALE CLOCKWORK TOYS

Almost every type of vehicle on the road represented; **some with electric lights**. Strongly constructed, and fitted with powerful, long-running mechanism, they will run anywhere, **even on the carpet**. Disc wheels, with rubber tyres. Each model is beautifully finished in a variety of colours, and packed singly in an attractive box. Various quantities according to type are packed in strong outer fibre cases for transit.

2845 MINIC Light Tank. Length 3¼″.

2822 MINIC Ford Royal Mail Van. Length 3⅜″.

2821 MINIC Ford £100 Saloon. Length 3½″.

2823 MINIC Ford Light Van. Length 3⅜″.

2835 MINIC Tractor. Length 3″.

2842 Vauxhall Cabriolet.

2841 Vauxhall Town Coupé.

2840 Vauxhall Tourer.

2851. Tourer with Passengers.

2824 MINIC Sports Saloon. Length 4¼″.

2856 MINIC Mechanical Horse and Trailer with cases. Length 7⅜″.

2830 MINIC Streamline Sports. Length 5″.

2825 MINIC Limousine. Length 4¼″.

2827 MINIC Town Coupé. Length 4¾″.

2866 MINIC Double-deck 'Bus. Length 7¼″. Red or Green.

2826 MINIC Cabriolet. Length 4¾″.

2831 MINIC Learner's Car. Length 4⅝″

2862 MINIC Single-deck 'Bus. Length 7¼″. Red or Green.

2839 MINIC Tip Lorry. Length 5½″.

2834 MINIC Delivery Lorry. Length 5½″.

2861 MINIC Searchlight Lorry with electric searchlight and battery. Length 5¼″

2865 MINIC Caravan Set (Tourer with passengers and Caravan with electric light). Overall length 9⅝″.
2857 MINIC Caravan with electric light and battery. Length 4¼″.

2860 MINIC Breakdown Lorry with Mechanical Crane. Length 5½″.

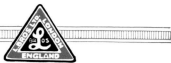

MINIC
2864 Rolls type Sedanca. With electric headlamps and battery. Length 5".
2858 Rolls type Sedanca. (Non-electric.)

MINIC
2852 Rolls type Tourer. (Non-electric.) Length 5".

MINIC 2854
Taxi. Length 4".

MINIC
2863 Daimler type Sedanca. With electric headlamps and battery. Length 5¼".
2859 Daimler type Sedanca. (Non-electric.)

MINIC
2853 Daimler type Tourer. (Non-electric.) Length 5¼".

2828 **MINIC** Open Touring Car. Length 4¾".

MINIC
2855 Caravan (non-electric) and Limousine. Overall Length 9⅝"
2833 Caravan (non-electric). Length 4¼".

2829 **MINIC** Streamline Saloon. Length 5".

2832 **MINIC** Racing Car. Length 5½".

2867 **MINIC** Fire Engine with electric headlamps and battery. Length 6¼".

2849 **MINIC** Dust Cart. Length 5⅛".

2843 **MINIC** Luton Transport Van. Length 5½".

2837 **MINIC** Tri-ang Transport Van. Length 5½".

2836 **MINIC** Petrol Tank Lorry. Length 5½".

2838 **MINIC** C. P. & Co. Van. Length 5½".

2848 **MINIC** Tractor and Trailer with cases. Length 7¼".

2844 **MINIC** Lorry with cases. Length 5½".

2847 **MINIC** Mechanical Horse and Fuel Oil Trailer. Length 7".

2850 **MINIC** Steam Roller. Length 5¼".

2846 **MINIC** Mechanical Horse and Pantechnicon. Length 7⅝".

MINIC CONSTRUCTION SET
ALL TO SCALE CLOCKWORK TOYS

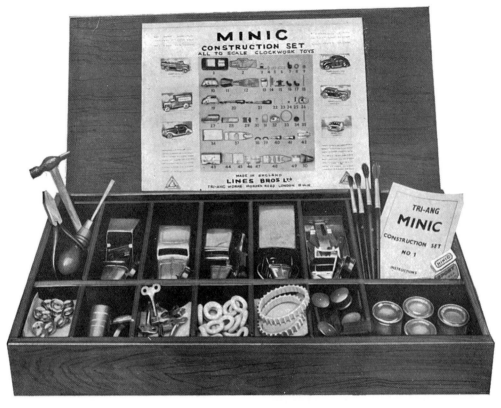

No. I MINIC CONSTRUCTION SET 2870

These kits enable the modern boy to build six types of MINIC all to scale clockwork toys. All parts, including powerful clockwork motor units, are made with precision tools and machines, thereby ensuring interchangeability. Rubber tyres, tools, brushes and enamel in various colours, together with full instructions for immediate assembly, are included in each kit, which is packed in a handsome oak finished cabinet $18'' \times 9\frac{3}{4}'' \times 2\frac{1}{2}''$.

MINIC
PRESENTATION SETS

ALL TO SCALE CLOCKWORK TOYS

MINIC PRESENTATION SET No. 1

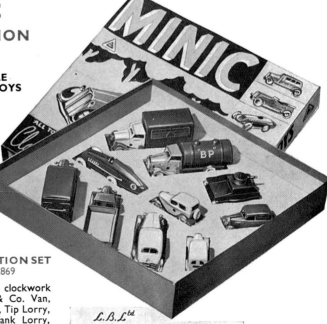

MINIC PRESENTATION SET No. 2 2869

MINIC PRESENTATION SET No. 1 2868

Containing all to scale clockwork toy models of Limousine, Cabriolet, Sports Saloon, Open Tourer, Ford £100 Saloon, attractively displayed in a strong decorated box $11\frac{1}{4}'' \times 11\frac{1}{4}'' \times 1\frac{5}{8}''$.

Containing all to scale clockwork toy models of C.P. & Co. Van, Tri-ang Transport Van, Tip Lorry, Racing Car, Petrol Tank Lorry, Limousine, Ford £100 Saloon, Ford Royal Mail Van, Ford Light Van and Light Tank, attractively displayed in a strong decorated box $15\frac{1}{4}'' \times 15\frac{1}{4}'' \times 2\frac{1}{2}''$.

Page Twenty-nine

CLOCKWORK LORRIES & VANS

Reliable clockwork motors. All bodies, etc., finished in bright colours. Metal wheels as illustrated. Remarkable value.

	2901			2897	
60	1	Steam Tip Lorry.	50	1	Motor Tip Lorry.

	2902			2898	
61	1	Steam Dust Cart. Length 9½".	51	1	Motor Dust Cart. Length 10¼".

	2903			2899	
62	1	Steam Milk Tanker. Length 8½".	52	1	Motor Petrol Tanker. Length 9½".

	2904			2900	
63	1	Steam Box Van. Length 8½".	53	1	Motor Box Van. Length 9¼".

2905

500 1 TRAILER. For use with any type in both Series. **Packed one in a carton printed in colours.** Length 5¾".

MOTOR LORRY FLEET (Not illustrated)

2906

Complete set of four toys and trailer of the 50 Series. Packed in display box.

STEAM LORRY FLEET (Not illustrated)

2907

Complete set of four toys and trailer, of the 60 Series. Packed in a display box.

LARGE LORRIES & VANS

		2908			2910	
203	4	STEAM BOX VAN	103	4	MOTOR DELIVERY VAN	
203	4E	**Ditto,** with two electric lights. Length 13¼".	103	4E	**Ditto,** with two electric lights. Length 13¼"
		2909			2911	
200	4	STEAM TIPPING LORRY	100	4	MOTOR TIPPING LORRY	
200	4E	**Ditto,** with two electric lights. Length 13⅜".	100	4E	**Ditto,** with two electric lights. Length 14¼"

2912

300 4 TRAILER
For either type.
Length 8".

The above is a series of well-known types of road vehicles. Specification includes long-running clockwork motor. Solid rubber wheels with metal discs. Pivoting front wheels. Strong metal chassis with attractive bodies, as illustrated. Electric light as specified. Packed one in a carton attractively printed in colours.

 YACHTS

STEEL HULLS

2913

"K" Yachts. Sizes 1, O, OO, OOO are **made with steel hulls,** like famous racing craft. They are fast and steady and will not capsize, even in the strongest wind. All sizes now have folding masts, dummy hatchways and bowsprits. Each yacht is finished in coloured synthetic enamel and is packed in a special carton printed in colours, complete with instructions.

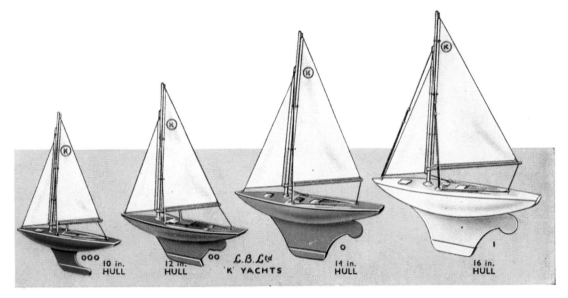

000 10 in. HULL   00 12 in. HULL   *L.B.L^{td}* 'K' YACHTS   O 14 in. HULL   1 16 in. HULL

L.B.L^{td} K 12 YACHT (Boxed fully rigged)

 YACHTS
GUARANTEED TO SAIL

SPECIAL FINISH
K YACHTS
BOXED   FULLY RIGGED

2914

MODELS K10, K12, K14 and K16

All steel hulls, beautifully finished in white and blue with red line. Folding masts and booms, made from specially selected wood. Best quality sails. Sold fully rigged in a handsome box with a blue background.

K10	... ...	hull 10"
K14	... ...	" 14"
K12	... ...	" 12"
K16	... ...	" 16"

PATENT
ONE-PIECE

HULL ON SIZES X and Y

2915

Splendid yachts, correctly rigged, Bermuda fashion, with best quality sails, and selected masts and boom. Metal keel with swinging rudder. Pressed hull nicely finished in white enamel, with contrasting colour band at waterline. Mahogany one-piece decks.

Size X	...	hull 18½"
Size Y	...	" 21"

SOLID WOOD HULL YACHTS

14", 18" and 20"  YACHTS

WITH SOLID WOOD HULLS

2916

A new range of inexpensive yachts with solid wood hulls and metal keels. The masts are folding and the bowsprits detachable. Nicely finished in attractive colours.

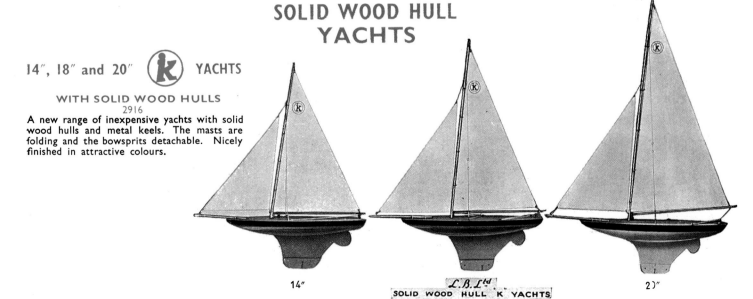

14"   *L.B.L^{td}* SOLID WOOD HULL K" YACHTS   20"
18"

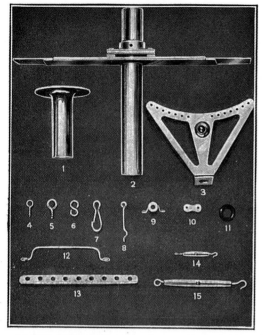

TRI-ANG RACING YACHTS

WITH AUTOMATIC STEERING

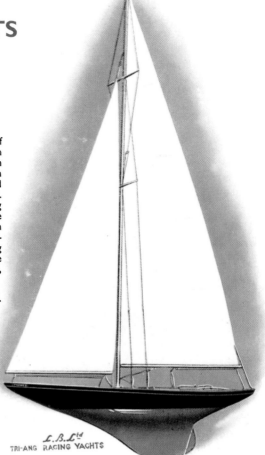

2918

Hand-built throughout to the lines of "J" class racing yachts, by craftsmen with sailing experience. Six sizes, each with Automatic Steering, Duralumin masts and booms. Correctly shaped sails and properly weighted lead keel. The three largest sizes have carrying handles inside the hatch and adjustable sliding masts. Each model is made from the finest selected materials, superlatively finished and packed in a strong well finished plywood box, complete with clamp stand. Six sizes : T24, T30, T36, T42, T48, T69.

Sizes of hulls : 24″, 30″, 36″, 42″, 48″, 69″.

Ⓚ YACHTS Ⓚ

L.B.L^td
TRI-ANG RACING YACHTS

SPARE FITTINGS FOR TRI-ANG RACING YACHTS

No.		No.	
1.	Fixed Mast Socket.	9.	Runner for Rudder Cords.
2.	Sliding Mast Socket.		
3.	Automatic Steering Quadrant.	10.	Rigging Bowsie.
4.	Small Screw Eye.	11.	Sheet Bowsie.
5.	Large Screw Eye.	12.	Sheet Horse.
6.	Rigging Hook.	13.	Jib Hook Rack.
7.	Rigging Clip.	14.	Small Rigging Screw
8.	Rudder Cord Hook.	15.	Large Rigging Screw

K4. ROSEMARY   *L.B.L^td* K YACHTS   K3. MARGARET   K2. ELIZABETH

"K" AUTOMATIC STEERING YACHTS   Models Nos. 2, 3 and 4.   2917

Magnificent craft. Patent lightweight, weather-resisting hull. Perfect balance wooden keel, lead weighted. Solid mahogany, polished deck. AUTOMATIC STEERING. Masts and booms made from the finest selected material. Best quality sails. Waterproof rigging cord ; brass fittings. Beautifully finished in blue and white. Nos. 3 and 4 have two-piece mast.

   K2 ELIZABETH ... hull 21″   K3 MARGARET ... hull 26″   K4 ROSEMARY ... hull 32″

 SPEEDBOATS

Strong wooden hulls and long running motors. Adjustable rudders, Dummy motor hatch. All sizes are fitted with windscreens. Sizes O and I with control lever and built-up hulls similar to No. 2. Finished in durable enamel in colours. Packed one in a carton printed in colours.

2919

OOO	...	...	...	...	10″ hull.
OO	...	...	...	...	11″ ,,
O	...	...	...	...	14″ ,,
I	...	...	...	...	16″ ,,

TRI-ANG SPEEDBOATS

Super Speedboats with specially designed hulls fitted with mahogany decks, brass fittings and ventilators. Nos. 3, 4 and 5 have a detachable motor cover, also bow pennant and stern flag. Model No. 2 is fitted with a powerful long distance clockwork motor. Models Nos. 3 and 4 are supplied either with clockwork or Electric motors, and Model No. 5 with electric motor only. All are beautifully finished, and have a special water resisting treatment. Sizes 3, 4 and 5 now fitted with propeller guards.

L. B. Ltd.
SPEEDBOATS

L. B. L^td
SPEEDBOAT Nº 2

2920
Clockwork motor. Length of hull, 18½″.

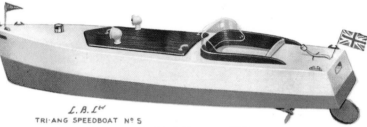

L. B. L^td
TRI-ANG SPEEDBOAT Nº 5
Electric motor. Length of hull 28″. 2923

3C	...	...	...	...	...	...	Fitted with Clockwork motor.	
3E	...	...	...	...	...	...	,, ,, Electric	,,
4C	...	...	...	...	...	...	,, ,, Clockwork	,,
4E	...	...	...	...	...	...	,, ,, Electric	,,
5E	...	...	...	...	...	...	,, ,, Electric	,,

TRI-ANG ELECTRIC CABIN CRUISERS

2924   Models of luxury Cabin Cruisers.

Fitted with illuminated cabin, port and starboard lights, detachable mahogany superstructure. Separate switches for motor and lights. Complete with ventilators, bow pennant and stern flag. Now fitted with propeller guard.

L. B. L^td
TRI-ANG SPEEDBOAT Nº 3

2921
Clockwork or electric motor. Length of hull, 20½″.

TRI-ANG SPEEDBOAT No. 4. Not illustrated. 2922
Similar to No. 3, clockwork or electric motor. Length of hull 23″.

L. B. L^td
CABIN CRUISER C

CABIN CRUISER "A"	Length of hull 20½″.
,, ,, "B"	,, ,, 23″
,, ,, "C"	,, ,, 28″
,, ,, "D"	,, ,, 40″

TRI-ANG ELECTRIC CABIN CRUISER "D"

2925

A scale model of a sea-going Cabin Cruiser. Raised fore-cabin and chart room. Bridge with screen and steering-wheel control on rudder. Tapered mast with rigging. Saloon has eight mica windows. Fore-cabin has eight brassed rounded portholes. Navigating light and fore-cabin also lit with **electric light.** Life-boat and two miniature life-belts. Two anchors, winch and chain locker. Rubbing strake from bow to stern. Length of hull 40″.

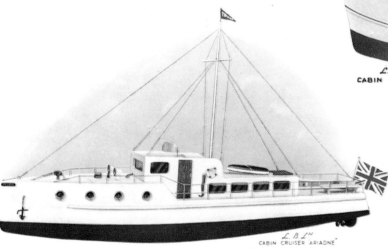

L. B. L^td
CABIN CRUISER ARIADNE

No. 3. COASTAL STEAMER "BRITISH MERCHANT"
2929

A magnificent model. Exceptionally strong clockwork motor. Working derricks and winding winches. Dummy ventilating shafts, portholes, navigating lights and lifebelts. Adjustable rudder. Two holds, with dummy cargo. Model working anchor, chain and winch. Adjustable pennant flags. Length of hull 29½". Finished in black and red with white superstructure.

SAILING FISHING SMACK
2931

Magnificent model with folding mast and boom. Adjustable sails, properly weighted lead keel. Supplied complete with Anchor. Specially suitable for shallow water. Length of hull 17".

No. I. COASTAL STEAMER.
" BRITISH TRADER "
2927
Realistic model with strong clockwork motor. Working derrick with winding winch. One hold complete with dummy cargo, adjustable rudder, anchor and chain, pennant flag, dummy lifebelt and portholes. Length of hull 17½". Finished in blue and red with brown super-structure.

No. 2. COASTAL STEAMER.
" BRITISH COMMERCE "
(Not illustrated)
2928
Similar to No. 1 but larger dimensions. Length of hull 22". Finished blue and red with white superstructure.

No. 0. COASTAL STEAMER (Not illustrated)
2926
New model with strong clockwork mechanism. One hold, working derrick and dummy lifebelt. Length of hull 13½".

TUG AND BARGE SET
2935

Novel bath set, absolutely "un-breakable. Made entirely of wood, with a cellulose finish in red. Overall length 25".

L.B. Ltd
TUG & BARGE SET

CLOCKWORK STEAM DRIFTER
2930

Realistic model with strong, long running clockwork mechanism, adjustable mizzen sail and rudder, dummy ventilators, etc. Length of hull 16½".

CHILDREN'S PLAYBOAT

Specially designed for children, the boat is extremely light in weight and easily carried. Buoyancy tanks have been fitted at each end to ensure safety.

L.B.Ltd
CHILDREN'S PLAYBOAT

CHILDREN'S PLAYBOAT   MODEL " C " (illustrated)
2934
Complete with buoyancy tanks, two hand operated paddle wheels, mast and sail, one pair oars, adjustable seat and footrest. This model can be used in a small area of water, as the independent paddles enable the boat to turn in its own length. Length 6' 2" Weight 38½ lbs. Finished red and blue.

MODEL " B " (Not illustrated.)   As " C " but without paddles. Weight 31 lbs.
2933
MODEL " A " (Not illustrated.)   As " C " but without paddles, mast and sail. Weight 29 lbs.
2932

TRI-ANG FIT BITS

Patented in most Countries.   TRADE MARK

"Fit-Bits" is something new in scientific toy construction. Hundreds of amusing models can be made, keeping kiddies amused for hours. All parts are beautifully coloured and fit together with patented rubber connections, making the figures flexible and life-like. **There are no sharp edges or metal parts.**

Fit-Bits will intrigue young-hearted people of all ages—few will be able to resist its attraction and mirth-provoking features. Each set is packed in a strong and attractively decorated box. All the sets illustrated are made from Fit-Bits

2937
No. 1A ATHLETE SET

2938
No. 2A ATHLETE SET

2939
No. 1FM FROG AND MOUSE SET

2936
No. 1SA SAILOR SET

2953
No. 1LG LIFEGUARD ON HORSE SET

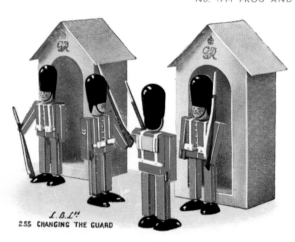

2952
No. 2SS CHANGING THE GUARD SET

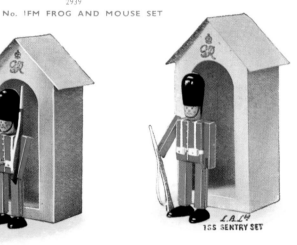

2951
No. 1SS SENTRY IN BOX

2956
No. 1SCB SULTAN AND COOLIE BOYS SET

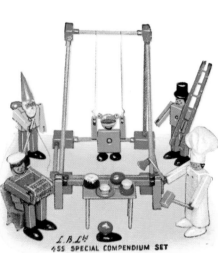

2944
No. 4SS SPECIAL COMPENDIUM SET

2954
No. 1C CIRCUS SET

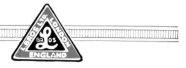

B
2974

C
2975

L.M.S. WOOD ENGINES

Realistic range of engines. Sizes B–E **NOW FITTED WITH STEEL DISC WHEELS AND RUBBER TYRES.** The drivers' cabs have curved tops and a whistle is fitted to each model.

Six 2″ disc wheels with rubber tyres. Length 16½″. Six in a box.

Six 2⅝″ disc wheels with rubber tyres. Length 18¾″. Each in a box.

2976   D

F
2978

Six 2⅜″ disc wheels with rubber tyres. Length 20½″. Each in box.

2977

E. (not illustrated.) Six 3″ disc wheels with rubber tyres. Length 28″. Each in box.

TRI-ANG LOCOS

F. Four 5″ driving wheels, four 3″ bogey wheels, steel with rubber tyres. Length 33½″. Each in box.

Very strongly constructed range of wooden engines, finished in red, green and yellow. All models fitted with steel wheels and rubber tyres.

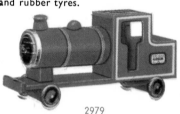

2979

2981

2983

No. 10. Four 1⅝″ wheels with rubber tyres. Twelve in a box.

No. 12. Four 2⅝″ wheels with rubber tyres. Twelve in a box.

No. 14. Four 2⅝″ wheels with rubber tyres. Singly boxed.

2980

2982

2984

No. 11. Four 2″ wheels with rubber tyres. Twelve in a box.

No. 13. Four 2⅝″ wheels with rubber tyres. Singly boxed.

No. 15. Four 3″ wheels with rubber tyres. Singly boxed.

MICKEY'S EXPRESS ENGINE   2985

One hundred smiles an hour! Realistic new engine with cut-out Mickey in the driving cab. Fitted with four steel disc wheels and rubber tyres. Complete with imitation smoke. Length 20″.

MICKEY FIVE-PIECE TRAIN SET   2986

This train set will give hours of amusement. There are no loose parts or hooks. Finished in washable cellulose enamel with amusing Mickey transfers. Overall length 30″.

TRI-ANG TRAIN SETS

L.B.L.td
M TRAIN SET

M TRAIN SET
2987

All-steel trucks, can be uncoupled, finished red and blue. Wood engine fitted with steel disc wheels and rubber tyres. Overall length 36½".

L.B.L.td
C TRAIN SET

C TRAIN SET
2988

Realistic set, wooden trucks, etc., one has working crane. Engine fitted with steel disc wheels and rubber tyres. Overall length 68½".

E TRAIN SET (Not illustrated)
2989

A large toy, almost unbreakable. Now fitted with 3" steel disc wheels and rubber tyres. Train uncoupled and linked by hook and chain. Overall length 92".

L.B.L.td
ROAD RIVER & RAIL SET

ROAD, RIVER AND RAIL SET
2990

This new set of toys will give hours of pleasure to children. Each model is propelled by an elastic motor. Very strongly constructed and nicely finished in cellulose colours.

"PUFF PUFF" ENGINES.

These strongly made "Locos" actually "puff-puff" as they are pulled along. Unbreakable mechanism is fitted to the front wheels. Fitted with rubber buffers back and front. Steel disc wheels with white rubber tyres. Wooden whistle included. **Finished in high gloss cellulose enamel.**

2991 No. 1. 4—4" wheels, chain, etc. Length 20½".
2992 No. 2. 6 wheels; 4—4"; 2—5". Length 23½".

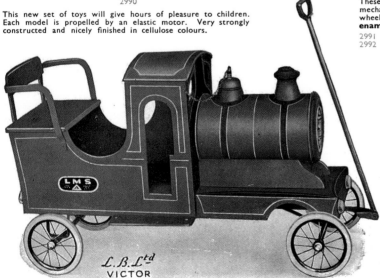

L.B.Ltd
VICTOR

"VICTOR" ENGINE
2993

Seats a young child. Pivoting front wheels, tubular pole for pulling. Tangent spoke wheels, ½" ribbed tyres. Safety backrest. Footplates. Attractively painted red and green, lined yellow. Length 38".

STEAM ROLLERS
2994

Four sizes. Well made and beautifully finished, steel tyred wheels and rollers. Flywheel revolves. Pivoting front roller. Nos. 1, 2 and 3 have chain and rubber ring. No. 4 has steel handle with wood grip. Painted red, green and black, lined yellow. Lengths: No. 1, 13½"; No. 2, 17"; No. 3, 19"; No. 4, 24".

HORSES

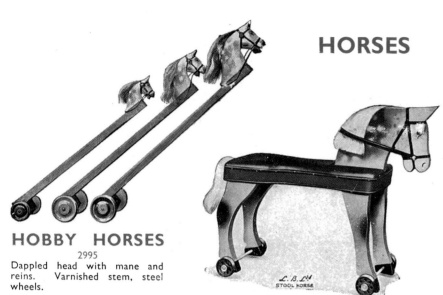

HOBBY HORSES
2995

Dappled head with mane and reins. Varnished stem, steel wheels.

Model	00	0	1	2
Lengths	28″	30″	33″	36″

STOOL HORSE
2996

A delightful toy for the toddler, upholstered seat 10″ from ground. Strongly made, dapple finish, cast wheels, mane and tail.

HOLLOW PUSH HORSES

HOLLOW PUSH HORSES
2997

Strongly made. Hollow wooden body. Nicely painted and dappled. Green base mounted on steel disc wheels with rubber tyres. Three sizes X, Y and Z. Height to handle : X 20½″, Y 24″, Z 26″.

"Z" HOLLOW ROCKING HORSE
2998

Very strongly made. Hollow wooden body. Nicely painted and dappled. Green base. Height to seat, 15¾″.

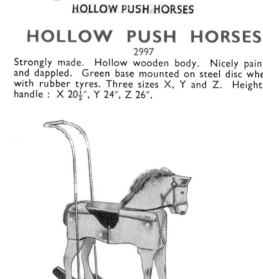

"Z" COMBINATION ROCKER AND PUSH HORSE
2999

Strongly made, nicely painted and dappled. Easily convertible either as a push horse or rocker. Fitted with 4″ rubber-tyred wheels. Height to handle 26″.

MICKEY MOUSE ROCKERS

By permission Walt Disney-Mickey Mouse, Ltd.

MICKEY SAFETY ROCKER
3001

Amusing new rocker. Very strongly constructed. Handle grips fitted to the head for safety. Brightly finished. Height to seat 20″.

MICKEY OLD STYLE ROCKER
3000

Very strongly constructed, fitted with handle grips for extra safety. Finished in bright colours. Height to seat 16″.

L.B.L.td PUSH HORSES
RUBBER TYRED WHEELS

"SPORTIBOY" SAFETY ROCKING HORSES 3002

Beautifully painted and dappled by experts. Constructed from well-seasoned timber. Saddles are detachable. Nicely varnished stand. Six sizes.

Model	...	...	1	2	3	4	5	6
Overall Length	...		36″	44″	52″	57″	64″	70″

PUSH HORSES 3003

Made of thoroughly seasoned timber, beautifully painted and dappled. Patent leather harness. Green base with steel disc wheels and rubber tyres. Handles of Nos. 1, 2 and 3 fold to facilitate packing in boxes. Four sizes.

Model ...	...	...	1	2	3	4
Height to handle	...		19½″	25½″	28½″	28″

L.B.LTD. OSR/1

OLD STYLE ROCKING HORSE 3004

One size only. Dappled horse, fitted with green curved base. Saddle not supplied. Suitable for a small child. Height to seat 16″.

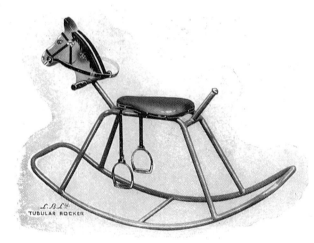

L.B.L.td TUBULAR ROCKER

TUBULAR ROCKER 3005

Strongly made of best quality steel tube, enamelled in blue. Well-padded saddle. Nicely finished head with handles fitted rubber grips. Height to seat 16¾″.

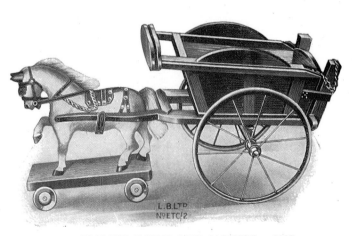

L.B.LTD No ETC/2

ELM TIP CARTS AND HORSES 3007

Practically unbreakable. Nicely varnished and fitted with tangent spoke wheels and rubber tyres. Steel disc wheels and rubber tyres to horses Nos. 3 and 4, which are well made and correctly dappled. Six sizes.

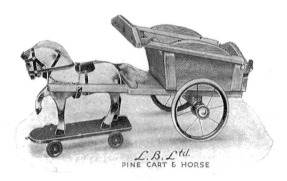

L.B.L.td.
PINE CART & HORSE

PINE TIP CARTS AND HORSES 3006

Very strongly made. Cart is now fitted with spoke wheels and rubber tyres and the horses disc wheels with rubber tyres. Four sizes : A, B, C, D. Two in a box.

TRI-ANG ROCKERS

L.B.Ltd
ROYAL JUMBO

ROYAL JUMBO
3009

Double sided rocker, with seat, play-tray and footrest. Elephant finished in grey with authentic Indian design in colour.

L.B.Ltd
COCK-A-DO ROCKER

COCK-A-DO ROCKER
3008

Novel design in rockers. Very suitable for the toddler. Nicely finished in green.

L.B.Ltd *Mister Quack*
MISTER QUACK ROCKER

MISTER QUACK ROCKER
3012

A new double sided rocker, very strongly made and beautifully finished in colour. Fitted with safety strap and hand bar.

L.B.Ltd
SHAGGY ROCKER

SHAGGY ROCKER
3010

A delightful new rocker, nicely coloured and fitted with seat, backrest and footrest. Can be propelled along by means of roller underneath.

L.B.Ltd
SWAN ROCKER

SWAN ROCKER
3011

Realistic design. Fitted with seat and play-tray. Nicely finished in white with contrasting markings. Cannot overturn.

KINDERGARTEN BUILDING BRICKS
3014

These full-size bricks will be welcomed by the children. Great fun and full of educational value. They are very strong and being hollow are also very light. There are 32 full-size bricks each 9″ × 4½″ × 2½″ and 16 half bricks each 4½″ × 4½″ × 2½″. Washable cellulose enamel finish, assorted blue, pink and white. Packed in a strong carton case. Size 18⅜″ × 13½″ × 18⅜″. Also supplied in unpainted wood.

L.B.Ltd
DOUBLE PUSH HORSE

DOUBLE PUSH HORSE
3013

Nicely coloured and fitted with steel disc wheels and rubber tyres. Chromium plated tubular handles. Seat and back with padded headrest.

BLACKBOARDS AND EASELS

3016

Nos. 1, 2, 3 and 4. New designs. Exceptionally well-made hardwood easels, fitted with chains, chalk rest and turned pegs. Sizes 1, 2 and 3 have 4½ mm. and size 4, 9 mm. plywood boards. Finished dull black with red lines. Each in a strong paper bag.

3015

No. A (Not illustrated). Strongly made. Deal easel, fitted with chain and pegs. Plywood board. Packed 12 in a box.

Blackboard sizes :

No. 1, 15″ × 11″ ;   No. 2, 18″ × 15″ ;
No. 3, 23¾″ × 17⅝″ ;   No. 4, 27″ × 21″ ;
No. A, 12″ × 10″.

MICKEY BLACKBOARD AND EASEL. No. 10

3017

A practical and cheerful nursery blackboard. Easel finished in washable cellulose enamel, and decorated with a Mickey Mouse schoolroom scene. Height 45½″.

MICKEY BLACK BOARD AND EASEL. No. 11

3013

Designed for the nursery—a blackboard and writing table combined. The blackboard swings down, forming a table with pigeon holes in which paper and envelopes can be kept. The easel and desk are finished in washable cellulose enamel and decorated with a Mickey Mouse school scene. Height 45½″.

MICKEY BLACKBOARD AND EASEL, No. 12

3019

Here is a novel and amusing blackboard, complete with cut-out Mickey. The easel is finished in washable cellulose enamel and Mickey in bright colours. Height 42½″.

WOOD PORTERS' TROLLEYS

3023

Made in three sizes: 0, 1 and 2; nicely varnished and strongly constructed. Steel disc wheels, rubber tyres. Lengths: 21½″, 25¾″ and 30¼″.

TUBULAR PORTERS' TROLLEY

3024

Strong but light, simply constructed of steel tube. Steel wheels, rubber tyres and handle grips. Enamelled blue, red wheels. Length 26½″.

SAND POLE CARTS

3010

Three sizes: 1, 2 and 3. Made of hardwood, lock cornered. Steel wheels have rubber tyres. Nicely varnished to show grain of wood. Packed two in a box. Improved finish. Lengths: 20″, 23″ and 27″.

"A" WOOD POLE CART

3021

Strongly made from hardwood, light finish. Red wooden wheels. Length 20¼″.

"B" AND "D" WOOD POLE CARTS

3022

Strongly made, with hinged seat, steel chassis and handle, fully sprung back axle. Steel disc wheels, rubber tyres. Lengths: B, 26″; D, 32″.

BARROWS

PINE BARROWS
3025

Re-designed with folding steel legs, to pack two in a box. Finished light varnish. Steel wheels rubber tyre. Five sizes: Nos. A, B, C, D, E. Lengths: A, 21″; B, 22½″; C, 25″; D, 27″; E, 32″.

MICKEY PAINTED BARROWS

Strongly made and fitted with steel disc wheels, rubber tyres, folding steel legs and finished in green and red with Mickey transfers. Four sizes: Nos. 1, 2, 3 and 4. Packed two in a box. For sizes see adjoining Nos. A, B, C, D.

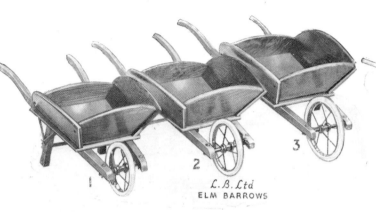

DEEP ELM BARROWS
3027

Very strong made and nicely varnished. Fitted with tangent spoke wheels and 1″ cushion tyres. Lengths: No. 10, 32″; No. 11, 35½″; No. 12, 36½″.

"SPORTIBOY" ELM BARROWS
3028

Varnish finish to show the fine elm grain. Tangent spoke wheels and 1″ cushion tyres now fitted. By loosening four bolts, legs can be folded to simplify packing. Very strong and realistic. Size 4 not illustrated. Lengths: No. 1, 31½″; No. 2, 35″; No. 3, 37½″; No. 4, 41″.

ALL-STEEL BARROWS
3029

Take apart to pack, six in a carton, no waste space. Finished green and black stove enamel. Rubber-tyred steel disc wheel, rubber handle grips. Remarkably low price, immensely strong. Two sizes. Lengths: Size 00, 23″; Size 0, 27″.

TRI-ANG DUMP WAGONS DE LUXE
3030

Made of steel throughout, very strong and well finished in stove enamel. Front wheels turn with handle. Body pivoted on rear wheels. Size of tray only is given. Three sizes. Lengths: No. 1, 20½″; No. 2, 23½″; No. 3, 26½″.

MICKEY BRICK BIN
3032

Ideal for the nursery, this brick bin is finished in bright colours, with Mickey transfers, and fitted with steel disc wheels and rubber tyres, also front castor. The bin is filled with Balsa wood, cut to various shapes. Height 20½″.

MICKEY BRICK TROLLEY
3033

Will keep the toddler amused for hours. Nicely finished in bright colours, it is fitted with steel disc wheels, rubber tyres and a strong front castor. The trolley is fitted with Balsa wood, cut to various shapes. Height to handle 20″.

2-WHEEL DUMP CART
3031

Strongly made, light varnish finish. Steel wheels, rubber tyres. Four sizes, all with adjustable handle. Lengths: No. 0, 31″; No. 1, 36½″; No. 2, 41″; No. 3, 46″.

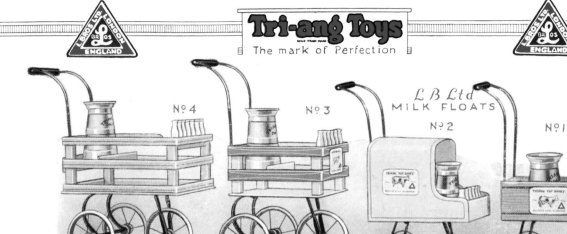
MILK FLOAT No. 4
3037

Strong construction. Fitted with 5″ spoke wheels and rubber tyres. Complete with churn and dummy milk bottles. Height 13¼″.

MILK FLOAT No. 3
3036

5″ spoke wheels, rubber tyres. Churn and dummy bottles. Height 12″.

MILK FLOAT No. 2
3035

New model, with churn, bottles and dummy packets. Fitted with disc wheels and rubber tyres. Height 10⅛″.

MILK FLOAT No. 1
3034

A low-priced toy complete with eight dummy bottles and churn with lid. Rubber tyres on disc wheels. Height 9¼″.

MILK FLOAT No. 5
3038

Strongly made toy complete with churn, two racks of dummy bottles, and fitted with disc wheels and rubber tyres Folding handle. Height 13¾″.

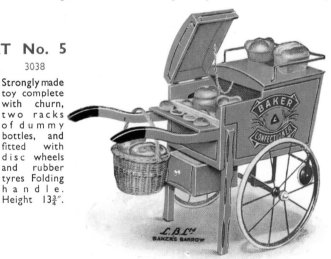

ICE CREAM BARROW   3039

Nicely made replica of well-known type. Correctly finished and complete with imitation ice cream bricks in strawberry and vanilla. Sizes 1 and 2. Heights: No.1 18″, No.2 23″.

BAKER'S BARROW No. 1
3040

Sliding tray inside, drawer below. Hinged top, rubber-tyred wheels, small wheel in front. Basket and four model loaves and four pastries included. Extra loaves and pastries at extra cost. Height 23″.

BARREL ORGAN   3043

Sizes A and B. A novel toy of sturdy construction, fitted with musical box and handle at rear of organ, also locker between handles. Finished in high gloss cellulose enamel. The monkey is not included, but can be obtained if required as an extra. Heights : Size A 14″, Size B 17½″.

BAKER'S BARROW No. 0
3041

Strongly constructed sliding tray, spoke wheels and rubber tyres. **NOT** supplied with bread and basket.

G.P.O. BARROW
3042

Strong red wicker basket, hinged, fitted in steel tube frame. Rubber tyres and handle grips. Parcels not included. Height 22″.

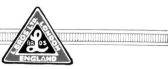

No. 2 GREENHOUSE

No. I
GREENHOUSE
3044

Fitted with hinged opening roofs and door. Includes shelves and central stand and 12 flower-pots, 12 saucers, six packets of seeds, water-can and pail. All windows and roof lights glazed. Finished white and green with imitation flower wall.

No. 2
GREENHOUSE
(Illustrated)
3045

As No. I, but with double tier centre stand. 18 flower-pots with saucers, 12 packets of seeds, watering-can and pail. Finished white and green with imitation flower wall.

COLD FRAME

COLD FRAME
3046

Sliding top light, fitted real glass in metal frames. Includes six flower-pots with saucers, six packets of seeds, one watering-can and pail. Finished white and green.

ELM GARDEN WAGON

GARDEN CART

ELM GARDEN WAGON
3050

A nicely made wagon with rubber-tyred tangent-spoke wheels and removable seat. Useful for a variety of purposes. Two sizes. Lengths overall 28" and 34".

GARDEN CART No. 2
(Illustrated)
3048

Contains everything required to cultivate a child's garden, especially made to size. Water tank with tap. Basket, watering-can, pail and tools. Rubber tyres.

GARDEN CART No. I
3047

Complete with tools, water tank and basket. Rubber-tyred wheels. Similar finish to No. 2.

GARDEN ROLLER
3049

Now greatly improved. Strong metal roller with hardwood handle, easy motion. Three sizes.

MICKEY PAINTED GARDEN WAGON
3051

Specially made for the young gardener. Fitted with steel disc wheels, rubber tyres and complete with spade, rake, trowel, small fork, watering-can and weeding basket. Finished in dark green and red, with Mickey transfers. Length 30½".

FARM WAGONS
3052

Strongly made of hardwood, now with closed ends of strong plywood. No. I has 4" × ½" steel disc wheels with rubber tyres. No. 2, 5½" × ½". No. 3, 6" × ½". Painted green with red wheels. Lengths 21½", 25" and 29".

DOLLS' COTS

DOLL'S COT 00
3053

Strongly made, with slatted sides. Drop side. Lath mattress. Bolster and overlay. Length 20¾".

DOLL'S COT 0
3053A

Similar to No. 00, but larger dimensions. Length 24½".

No. 1 DOLL'S COT
3054

Exceptionally well made and fitted with spring mattress. Drop side, with nickel-plated fittings and strong castors. Well stuffed overlay and bolster. Finished in washable cellulose enamel in various colours. Length 20¾".

No. 2 DOLL'S COT   3055

Similar to No. 1, but larger dimensions. Length 24¾".

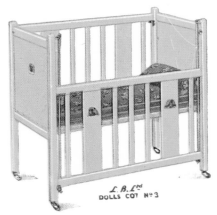

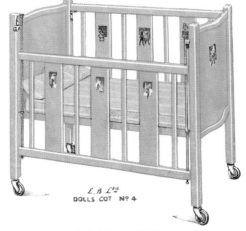

No. 3 DOLL'S COT
3056

Splendid new cot with four panels, slats and fully enclosed ends decorated with transfers. Spring mattress, drop side, nickel-plated fittings and strong castors. The overlay and bolster have been greatly improved. Finished in washable cellulose enamel in various colours. Length 26¾".

MICKEY DOLL'S COT
3058

Exceptionally well made, drop side, nickel-plated fittings, strong castors, well stuffed mattress and bolster. Finished in washable cellulose colours. Length 20½".

No. 4 DOLL'S COT   3057

A really luxurious new doll's cot with panels, slats and fully enclosed shaped ends. Fitted with extra strong spring mattress. Drop side, with nickel-plated fittings, and improved overlay and bolster. Finished in washable cellulose enamel. Length 31".

MICKEY DOLL'S BED
3059

Strongly made and nicely finished in colours. Mickey transfers at each end. Two sizes : A, length 20¾". B, length 25½".

"COSY" DOLLS' COTS
3060

Enamelled steel frame, draped bed with mattress and pillow. Folds flat. Packs in a box. Two sizes. No. 1, length 19". No. 2, length 22½".

I. B. Ltd.
KITCHENETTE No. 2

KITCHENETTES, ETC.

L.B.Ltd
No. 1 TOY DRESSER

L. B. Ltd.
KITCHENETTE No.

No. 2 KITCHENETTE

3062

Fitted with flour sifter, three large and four small enamelled containers, two drawers, cupboard, pull-out pastry-board, two moulds and grater, dustpan and brush, and brown glazed earthenware mixing bowl. Finished blue, white or pink. Height $21\frac{1}{2}$ ins.

No. 1 TOY DRESSER

Strongly made, with a dark oak finish. Fitted with three drawers and two shelves. Height $21\frac{1}{4}$ ins.

No. 1C TOY DRESSER

Similar to No. 1, but finished in cellulose colours.

No. 3 KITCHENETTE

3063

Attractively equipped model with flour-sifter, twelve large enamel containers, six small ditto, aluminium colander, saucepan, kettle, glazed earthenware mixing bowl, china dish, breadboard, grater and two moulds, pull-out pastry-board, two drawers, fitted enamel breadbin, white enamel bowl, dustpan and brush, crumb brush and tray, and mincer. Finished blue, white or pink. Height $30\frac{1}{4}$ ins.

L.B.L.
KITCHENETTE JUNIOR

L. B. L.
WRINGER SET

SCULLERY SINK

3065

A nicely made toy, with two separate tanks for hot and cold water. Plate rack, sink with drain plug, and draining board. Two cupboards and drawer. Pail to hold waste water. Finished in white cellulose enamel. Height $30\frac{3}{4}$ ins.

Page Fifty

KITCHENETTE No. 1 (JUNIOR)

3061

Painted pink, complete with canisters, heavy aluminium kettle, colander and saucepan. Height 15 ins.

LAUNDRY SET

3066

A very attractive line with wringer, clothes-horse, galvanized bath and pail, and scrubbing board. Wringer, 19 ins. high.

TRI-ANG WRINGER

3067

Very useful to the young housewife. Steel frame enamelled green, mounted on cast wheels. Hardwood rollers.

COOKERY SETS, ETC.

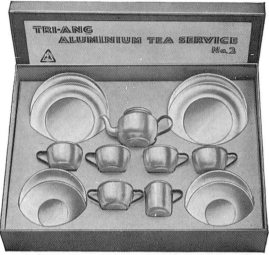

ALUMINIUM TEA SERVICE No. 2
3070

Packed in attractive box. Contents : teapot with lid, four cups and saucers, four die-cast spoons, cream jug, sugar basin, four plates, all in polished aluminium.

YOUNG HELPER'S SET No. 3
(Aluminium)
3069

Packed in attractive box. Contents : rying pan, porringer (three pieces), stew-pan and steamer (three pieces), kettle (two pieces), colander, all in polished aluminium.

LITTLE HELPER'S PASTRY SET
3068

Contents : pastry board, roller, wood spoon, mixing basin, pie dish. Packed in attractive box.

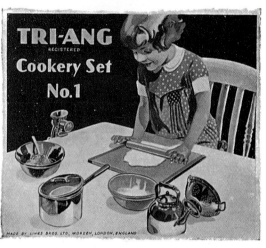

COOKERY SET
3071

Packed in attractive box measuring 13½ × 12″ × 4½″. Includes mincer, saucepan, kettle, colander in aluminium. pudding basin, pie dish, rolling pin and board.

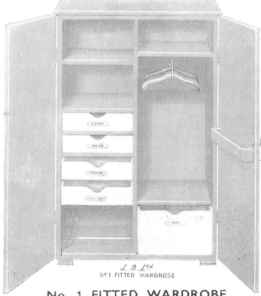

No. 1 FITTED WARDROBE
3072

A splendid piece of dolls' furniture, fitted with coat hangers, four drawers, shelves and shoe rack. Nicely finished in cellulose enamel. Various colours. Now fitted with mirror inside door. Height 21¾″.

CHEST OF DRAWERS
3073

A well designed range of beautifully made dolls' furniture. There are three sizes each fitted with three drawers and nicely finished in cellulose colours. Heights : No. 1 12″, No. 2 15⅛″, No. 3 18⅛″.

TALLBOY
3074

A particularly well made piece of dolls' furniture. Fitted with six drawers and nicely finished in cellulose colours. Height 28¼″.

DINNER WAGGON
3075

Strong hardwood construction. Nicely finished in colours. **Both sides take apart and pack flat.** Fitted small castors. Height No. 1 19″.

Page Fifty-one

DOLLS' FURNITURE SETS

*L.B.L*ᵗᵈ
FURNITURE SET SIZE 0

FURNITURE SET SIZE 0

3076

Set comprises table and two chairs. Finished in blue or pink. Folding table 11" high.

*L.B.L*ᵗᵈ
FURNITURE SET No. 1

FURNITURE SET No. 1

3077

Hardwood construction. Two chairs and folding table   Blue or pink cellulose enamel finish.

*L.B.L*ᵗᵈ
ARMCHAIR

*L.B.L*ᵗⁱ
CURATE

CURATE

3080

Very fashionable addition to the furniture set, sturdily built of hardwood. Dark oak finish.

ARMCHAIR

3079

Well made from hardwood. Turned legs. Shaped seat. Very comfortable. Finished in dark oak. Packed in fibreboard case.

*L.B.L*ᵗᵈ
MICKEY DOLLS HIGH CHAIR
BY PERMISSION WALT DISNEY · MICKEY MOUSE LTD

DOLL'S HIGH CHAIR No. 1

3081

Has two positions. Vertical, as illustrated, and folds in centre to bring playing tray and wheels into use. Made in hardwood, finished blue or pink.

MICKEY DOLL'S HIGH CHAIR

3082

Has two positions, can be folded, bringing into use playing tray. Nicely finished in washable cellulose enamel and decorated with Mickey transfer.   Height 24½".

FURNITURE SET No. 2

3078

Shaped seats to chairs. Table has two gate legs and two fixed, a really nice piece of furniture. Makes a novel coffee stool. Finished dark oak. Packed in fibreboard box. (Tables and chairs can be purchased separately.) Also obtainable in colours.

DESKS

No. 5T TUBULAR DESK AND SEAT
3083

New low-priced model, strongly constructed and fitted with inkwell. Tubular frame to desk. Stove enamelled green. Height of desk 22½".
6T. Similar to above, but desk finished in colour and seat upholstered.

No. 9T TUBULAR DESK AND SEAT
3085

Exceptional value. Fitted with sliding inkwell cover. Strong tubular frame with back cross member, and foot-rest, complete with upholstered seat, tubular frame. Tubular work enamelled in colour; woodwork dark finish. Height of desk 28½".

No. 10T (Not illustrated)
3086

As No. 9T, but woodwork finished in colour and fitted with **chromium plated** inkwell cover and hinges.

No. 11T (Not illustrated)
3087

Similar to No. 10T, but all tubular work **chromium plated.**

No. 7T TUBULAR DESK AND SEAT
3084

New model, fitted with inkwell and strong tubular frame, stove enamelled. Seat also has tubular frame and is nicely upholstered. Height of desk 26½".
8T. Similar to above, but desk in colour.

No. 1 KNEEHOLE DESK AND CHAIR
3090

Exceptionally well made, with dark oak finish. Fitted with centre drawer and supplied with pen rack and inkwell. Chair is nicely upholstered. Height of desk 25".

No. 2 KNEEHOLE DESK AND CHAIR
3091

Very strong construction, with dark oak finish. Fitted with seven drawers, pen rack and inkwell. Chair is nicely upholstered. Height of desk 24".

No. 13 DESK AND SEAT
3089

New model, finished in cream. Desk fitted with inkwell and chromium plated sliding cover. Seat nicely uphol-stered. Height of desk 24½".

No. 12T TUBULAR DESK AND SEAT
3088

Handsome new desk finished in blue, with two inkwells. The tubular framework of desk and chair are **chromium plated** and the chair is well upholstered in ivory leather-cloth. Height of desk 28½".

No. 4 KNEEHOLE DESK AND HARDWOOD CHAIR
3092

Constructed chiefly from oak, dark finish, fitted with nine drawers and complete with blotting pad and pen rack, with two inkwells. **Now supplied with Hard-wood Chair.** Height of desk 24½".

A. BUREAU AND SEAT
3093

Strongly constructed. Flap with lock and key. Pigeon holes, pen rack and inkwell. Two useful shelves. Complete with seat. Light finish. Height of desk 30⅜″.

B. ROLL TOP DESK
AND HARDWOOD CHAIR
3096

A handsome piece of furniture, strongly constructed chiefly from oak, dark finish. Fitted with pigeon holes and nine drawers. Complete with blotting pad and pen rack with two inkwells. Now supplied with Hardwood Chair. Height of Desk 31¼″.

A. ROLL TOP DESK AND SEAT
3095

Strongly constructed, light finish. Fitted with pigeon holes, pen rack and inkwell. Complete with Seat. Height of Desk 28¼″.

B. BUREAU AND HARDWOOD CHAIR
3094

Constructed chiefly from oak, dark finish. Fitted with pigeon holes. Flap with lock and key, pen rack and two inkwells. Two useful shelves underneath. Now supplied with Hardwood Chair. Height of Desk 33¼″.

MICKEY DESK AND CHAIR
3098

Strongly made and beautifully finished in washable cellulose enamel. The desk has a hinged lid and is fitted with sliding inkwell cover. Ideal for the modern nursery. Height of Desk 24½″.

HARDWOOD CHAIR
3097

Very strong construction, dark oak finish. Upholstered seat.

CLIMBING FRAME
3099

An excellent safe climbing device. Stands firm when erected and folds flat when not required. Hardwood construction. A constant source of exercise and amusement.

PLAY CASTLE
3100

Absolute safety or very young children. A combined chute and climbing device. Rigid hardwood construction.

RAIL SWING
3101

Wood strips and beads, threaded on ropes. Rails lift up to seat child. Complete with ropes and rings. Varnish finish.

"D" RAIL SWING
3102

Ideal for the nursery, beautifully finished in blue with large coloured beads. Complete with coloured ropes and rings.

CHAIR SWINGS
3103

Comfortably shaped and safe for the youngest child. Bar in front slides up. Gaily coloured ropes with rings included. Blue enamel finish. Three sizes, Nos. 1, 2, 3.

BABY'S SAFETY CANVAS SWING
3104

Swing specification as Frame Swing. This is suitable for use in the nursery. Hooks are provided. Can be hung from door frame.

"A" FRAME SWING
3105

New model with strong tubular frame, stove enamelled green, comfortable seat made of wood. Supplied with steel pegs for fixing into ground. Height 43½ ins.

"C" FRAME SWING
3106

Similar to No. A. Canvas seat sewn on steel frame, with tray and coloured beads. Spring suspension. Folding tubular steel stand, enamelled blue. Very rigid, strong and light. Height 57½ ins.

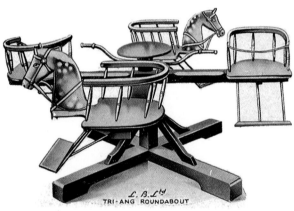

ROUNDABOUT
3109

Four seats, two with horse-heads. The children on the other seats pull the roundabout round by the handles at the side of the centre table. Nicely painted in colours. Length 66 ins. Height 28 ins.

No. I SAND TRAY
3107

Nicely made with strong awning in striped canvas. Two well-made stools (which can also be used in the nursery are included).

42 ins. square.
65 ins. high.

No. 0 SAND TRAY
3108

(Not illustrated). Similar to No. I but cheaper quality.

SWITCHBACK
3110

The Switchback has successfully met the demand for an outdoor plaything of absolute safety for very young children. The trolley, constructed of wood, with a steel undercarriage, has four 3" solid steel ball-bearing wheels, flanged to fit the track, making it impossible to de-rail. Upholstered leather seat and hand-brake acting on the rear wheels. Track (built in 8-ft. sections, to facilitate transit) is constructed of finest seasoned hardwood, stained with three coats of weatherproof solution. Can be extended to any length by attaching extra sections (at extra cost). Packs in two crates: 20½"×3′ 6″×2′ 4″ and 8′ 3″×1′ 0″×2′ 0″.

TRI-ANG FORTS

No. 0 FORT
3119

Castle design on imitation rock base. Drawbridge and separate ramp. All parts pack in base. Length 12″.

No. 00 FORT (Not illustrated).
3118

Castle design on imitation rock base. Self-contained ramp. Wonderful value. All parts pack in base. Length 10½″.

L.B.Ltd 'B' FORT

No. B FORT
3117

Strongly made, fitted with ramp, drawbridge and portcullis. All parts pack into base. Length 18″.

No. A FORT
3116
(Not illustrated.)
Castle design, with ramp and drawbridge. All parts pack into base. Length 14″.

No. 3 FORT *L.B. Ltd.*
3123 FORT No. 3.

Imitation rock base. Three model spring cannons, drawbridge and separate ramp. Four flashing red electric lights in hollow tower, also with imitation gun-fire noise device. Batteries not supplied. Towers detach for packing. Length 17½″.

FORT No. 1
3120

Castle design, includes flagstaff, ramp and drawbridge. All parts packed in base. Fitted for electric light, but without battery. Length 12″.

No. 4 FORT
3124

Imitation rock base. Four model spring gun turrets, drawbridge, separate double ramp and flagstaff. Fitted with six flashing red electric lights in hollow towers and imitation gun-fire noise device. Batteries not included. Length 28½″.

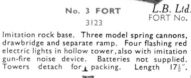

L.B. Ltd.
FORT No. 1A.

No. 1A FORT
3121

Drawbridge and one spring model cannon. All parts pack in base. Fitted with electric light, but without battery. Length 16¼″.

  No. 2 FORT
3122

Castle design. Self-contained moat, ramps, drawbridge and flagstaff. Two spring model cannons. All parts pack in base. Fitted with electric light, but without battery. Length 22⅜″.

L.B.L⁴ᵈ
SEE SAW ROUNDABOUT

 **FOLDING SEE SAW ROUNDABOUT**
3114

A very soundly constructed garden toy combining a sea saw and roundabout. The wooden seats are fitted with hand grips. Overall length 8′.

L.B.L⁴ᵈ
RAIL CHUTE

RAIL CHUTE. 3111

Strongly made, takes apart and is easily stored. Size No. 1. Length of chute 6′ 8″. Height 3′ 11″. Size No. 2. Length 8′ 4″. Height 4′ 6″.

LARGE CHUTE. 3112 (Not illustrated.) A popular garden toy. Weatherproofed hardwood, braced with steel. Cannot overturn. Dismantles and packs into small space. (It is strongly advisable to cover the chute over in wet weather to protect the slide from dampness, otherwise we cannot guarantee they will give good service.) Length of chute 11′. Height 6′ 9″.

SEE SAW CHUTE 3113 (Not illustrated). Combined see saw and chute. Very strongly constructed from hardwood. Length 9′. Height 4′ 10″.

L.B.L⁴ᵈ
SEE SAW

SEE SAWS
3115

Improved models, now have hand grip. Strongly made of varnished hardwood, on rigid steel stand, enamelled red. Coil spring at each end prevents jars and increases the enjoyment. Two sizes: No. 1, length 56″; No. 2, length 74″.

L. B. Ltd.
NO. 1 THEATRE

TRI-ANG THEATRES

No. 1 THEATRE
3125

Two electric footlights with switch at rear of stage. Pelmet and roll-up velvet curtain. Front and rear arches hinged. Complete with specially written play, stage directions, scenery, characters and properties in full colour. Packed in a strong lidded box. Height 15⅜ ins. **Extra plays and scenery for Theatres can be supplied at additional cost.**

L. B. Ltd.
NO. 2 THEATRE

No. 3 THEATRE
3127

A very handsome production with proscenium arch finished in cream and gold. Electric footlights and **two spotlights with rotating vari-coloured discs.** Independent switches for footlights and spotlights. Pelmet and roll-up velvet curtain. Hinged front and rear for easy erection. A special velvet screen for sides and back, which conceals operators, is provided with this model. Orchestra pit, rail and velvet curtain. Complete with three specially written plays with stage instructions. All scenery and characters in full colours. Height without curtain 20½ ins. Packed in a box.

> TRANSFORMERS FOR OPERATING ELECTRIC LIGHTS FROM THE MAINS CAN BE OBTAINED
> AC ONLY.

L. B. Ltd.
NO. 3 THEATRE

No. 2 THEATRE
3126

Smartly finished proscenium arch in black and silver, with special pelmet. Electric footlights and **spotlights with rotating vari-coloured discs.** Roll-up velvet curtain, orchestra pit velvet curtain. Hinged front and rear for easy assembly. Complete with **two specially** written plays, with stage directions. Scenery, characters and props in full colours. Height 18⅛ ins. Packed in a box.

L. B. Ltd.
E TRI-ANG STORES

TRI-ANG STORES
3128

A delightful range of Children's Shops. Each complete with scales, dummy bottles and boxes. Five sizes, all fitted with drawers and name tabs. No. D has glass windows and sliding glass partition. No. E has glass windows and roll shutter, as illustrated. Beautifully finished in contrasting colours.

L. B. Ltd.
TRI-ANG STORES A

L. B. Ltd.
TRI-ANG STORES C

Heights: A 14⅞ ins., B 24 ins., C 29¾ ins., D 28½ ins., E 32¾ ins.

SCALE MODEL PERIOD DOLLS' FURNITURE

(Trade Mark)

ACTUAL SCALE MODEL REPRODUCTIONS QUEEN ANNE AND JACOBEAN STYLES

All Queen Anne models have beautiful walnut finish

All Jacobean models finished dark oak

J53
Jacobean **Period** Scale Model
FOUR-POSTER BED
Complete with down-proof sateen curtains, canopy, coverlet and bolster. Four turned posts and solid base.

QA14
Queen Anne **Period** Scale Model
DINING ROOM TABLE
Oval top, Cabriole legs, highly finished.

J55
Jacobean **Period** Scale Model
ARMCHAIR
With velvet seat and back. Bobbin turned legs and front rod.

QA6
Queen Anne **Period** Scale
FIRESCREEN
Screen covered floral design.

J51
Jacobean **Period** Scale Model
CHAIR No. 3
With velvet seat and back. Bobbin turned legs.

QA13
Queen Anne **Period** Scale Model
HANGING MIRROR
Should be hung over Console Table.

QA11
Queen Anne **Period** Scale Model
CONSOLE TABLE
Polished top, graceful Cabriole legs.

J54
Jacobean **Period** Scale Model
OAK CHEST
Hinged lid, plain panels divided by stiles.

Jacobean Period Scale Model DINING ROOM SET No. 2
Containing four Chairs No. 4, J52; two Armchairs, J56; Court Cupboard, J50; Refectory Table, J59. The Set complete is packed in a handsome box, or each piece can be obtained separately. **Bedroom Sets** are also obtainable.

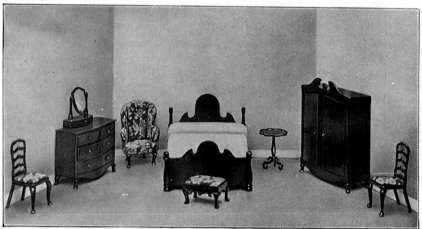

Queen Anne Period Scale Model BEDROOM SET
Containing Bedstead, QA17; Wardrobe, QA16; Chest of Drawers, QA19; Dressing Mirror No. 1, QA18; two Chairs No. 2, QA4; Easy Chair, QA8; Footstool, QA15; Occasional Table, QA12. The complete set is packed in a handsome box, or each piece can be obtained separately. **Dining Room and Drawing Room Sets** are also obtainable.

QA7
Queen Anne **Period** Scale Model
CHINA CABINET
With interior shelves and transparent opening doors. Cabriole legs. Finished with Whorl grain markings.

Perfect proportion was one of the keynotes in the Queen Anne **Period**, this has been faithfully reproduced in the **Period** scale model Furniture.

Each piece of **Period** Scale Model Furniture is packed in a handsome box.

Queen Anne CONSTRUCTIONAL DRAWING ROOM SET (Illustrated)
CONSTRUCTIONAL SETS
Queen Anne **DRAWING ROOM SET**
Queen Anne **BEDROOM SUITE**
Each piece is delicately cut out and shaped. The set is complete with stain, lacquer, upholstery and full equipment, also step by step instruction leaflet for making this wonderful scale model **Period** Furniture.

QA1
Queen Anne **Period** Scale Model
DINING CABINET
Fitted shelves and two opening doors. Cabriole legs.

Queen Anne Chairs and Settee are covered in floral material (an exact copy of the early petit-point pattern). All the furniture has beautifully turned Cabriole legs, a leading characteristic of the period.

QA9
Queen Anne **Period** Scale Model
SETTEE
Shaped sides and back. Upholstered to match Easy Chair. Short Cabriole legs.

QA10
Queen Anne **Period** Scale Model
SIDE TABLE
Imitation marble top. Cabriole legs.

QA3
Queen Anne **Period** Scale Model
WRITING ARMCHAIR
Gracefully shaped solid slat, seat covered with floral material. Beautifully turned Cabriole legs.

QA5
Queen Anne **Period** Scale Model
CHAIR No. 1
Cabriole legs, seat upholstered floral design.

J57
Jacobean **Period** Scale Model
DRESSING MIRROR No. 2
Adjustable position, turned arms and shaped base.

J58
Jacobean **Period** Scale Model
SIDE TABLE
Half hexagon top, four turned legs with square feet.

QA2
Queen Anne **Period** Scale Model
WRITING BUREAU
Two drawers, fall flap, inside fitted pigeon holes. Short Cabriole legs.

SCALE MODEL PERIOD DOLLS' FURNITURE
(Trade Mark)

MUSIC STOOL
QA22
A particularly well-made piece. Walnut or ebony piano finish.

UPRIGHT PIANO
QA21
A handsome piece for the Doll's House. The keyboard cover is hinged and shuts up. Beautiful walnut or ebony piano finish.

DRESSER AND PLATES
QA23
Fitted with two drawers, Cabriole legs. Beautiful walnut finish.

GRAND PIANO
QA20
Beautifully made scale model. Cabriole legs, hinged covers and music rest. Walnut or ebony piano finish.

FIREPLACE
With Electric Fire.
J61
Scale model reproduction of Old English Fireplace, with fire dogs and realistic fire effect. Complete with battery.

MONK'S BENCH
J63
Scale model of a genuine museum piece. Turned legs. Dark oak finish.

DRAWLEAF TABLE
J62
A particularly well-made piece. Turned legs with rigid cross member. Table top can be extended. Dark oak finish.

FIREPLACE
J60
Imitation bricks and complete with fire dogs. Cream with oak finish mantelpiece.

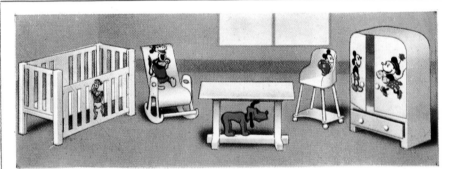

By Permission Walt Disney Mickey Mouse, Ltd.

MICKEY DOLL'S NURSERY SUITE
This charming set of Doll's House Furniture includes: Cot with drop side, Rocking Chair, Table with cut-out of Pluto underneath, High Chair, Cupboard with opening doors, shelves and a drawer. Packed in a handsome box.

MODERN FURNITURE SET
Modern furniture for the modern doll's house. Bright metal tubular framework, upholstered chairs and armchairs. Highly finished table top.

KNOLE SUITE
A delightful suite in miniature of a well-known Tudor design. Both settee and armchairs are beautifully upholstered in rich scarlet and gold.

No. 1 JACOBEAN BEDROOM SET
The set includes Bed complete with canopy, coverlet and bolster. Two Chairs with bobbin turned legs and fireplace. Packed in a handsome box.

No. 1 JACOBEAN DINING ROOM SET
The set includes Table with turned legs, four Chairs with bobbin turned front legs and engraved back, also fireplace. Packed in a handsome box.

TRI-ANG
DOLLS' HOUSES

3129
DOLLS' HOUSE No. 20

Low priced model with opening metal-framed windows and front door. Imitation tiled roof, brick sides and front with balcony. Front hinged to open. Height 14¾". Length 9¼".

3131
DOLLS' HOUSE No. 22

Larger model. Opening metal-framed windows and imitation green shutters. Tiled roof, brick sides and front with spacious balcony. Front hinged to open. Height 16½". Length 13¼".

3130
DOLLS' HOUSE No. 21

New design with opening metal-framed windows and imitation shutters. Realistic tiled roof, brick sides and front with balcony. Front hinged to open. Height 16½". Length 10¼".

3132
DOLLS' HOUSE No. 23

Attractive new model. Two rooms, imitation tiled roof, opening metal-framed windows. Sun porch and nicely flowered front. Hinged opening front. Height 16¼". Length 13¾".

> Each Dolls' House is packed in a strong container.

3134
DOLLS' HOUSE No. 45

Four rooms fitted with dummy fireplaces and electric wall lights. One room has an inglenook, with winding staircase. Garage with opening doors. Balcony, front door and metal framed windows.

3133
DOLLS' HOUSE No. 24

Wonderful value. Imitation half timbered gable. Metal-framed windows with curtains, imitation shutters, tiled roof and brick front with spacious balcony. Four rooms and staircase. Front hinged to open in two places. Height 22". Length 22".

ULTRA MODERN DOLLS' HOUSES

DOLLS HOUSE Nº 49

DOLLS HOUSE Nº 50

DOLLS HOUSE Nº 51

3135

3136

3137

No. 49. Modern design with opening front. Two rooms, fitted with electric wall lights. Built-in garage, with opening doors. Metal framed windows. Finished in cream and green. Length 18 ins.

No. 50. Ultra modern design with opening front. Movable suntrap. Two rooms fitted with electric wall lights, fireplaces and metal framed windows. Opening front door with staircase. Built-in garage, with opening doors. Finished in cream and green. Length 21 ins.

No. 51. A larger house. Four rooms fitted with fireplaces and electric wall lights. Built-in garage, with opening doors. Metal framed windows. Finished in cream and green. Length 29 ins.

DOLLS HOUSE Nº 52

BATTERIES ARE NOT INCLUDED FOR ELECTRIC LIGHT MODELS

DOLLS HOUSE Nº 53

3138

3139

No. 52. Two large rooms fitted with fireplaces and electric wall lights. Metal framed windows front and side. Built-in garage, with opening doors. Movable suntrap, opening front. Beautifully finished in cream and green, with imitation crazy paving. Length 33 ins.

No. 53. Four large rooms, fitted with fireplaces, electric wall lights. Metal framed windows, door leading out to verandah. Kitchen fitted with dummy gas stove, sink and dresser. Built-in garage. Movable suntrap, opening front. Finished in cream and green, with imitation crazy paving. Length 52 ins.

DOLLS HOUSE Nº 60

3140

No. 60. A well-made house at a popular price. Opening metal framed windows, two rooms (with electric wall lights), tiled sun-porch, steps and dummy shrubs. **Red-tiled roof.** Now greatly improved with addition of window box. Length 13¾ ins.

3141

No. 61. A larger house with built-in garage, two large rooms (with electric wall lights), metal framed windows, tiled sun-porch, steps and dummy shrubs. **Grey-tiled roof.** Now greatly improved with addition of window box. Length 19 ins.

3142

No. 62. (Not illustrated.) Large double-fronted model with four rooms and staircase, built-in garage, opening metal framed windows, **red-tiled roof**, steps and dummy shrubs, four electric wall lights, nicely flowered front, both gables have half-timbered effect. Now greatly improved with addition of window box. Length 26⅜ ins.

DOLLS HOUSE Nº 61

SPECIAL FEATURES
HALF-TIMBERED GABLES & FRONT
IMITATION FLOWERED FRONTS
REALISTIC GREEN SHUTTERS
TILING ON ROOFS EMBOSSED
METAL FRAMED WINDOWS
EACH DOLL'S HOUSE IS PACKED
IN A STRONG CONTAINER

TRANSFORMERS can now be obtained for working all Dolls' Houses with electric lights from the mains.

DOLLS' HOUSE

3143

No. 91. Entirely new design. Hinged front, opening in three sections. Five rooms, including bathroom with dummy bath. Dummy fireplaces. Two electric wall lights. Garage. Opening metal-framed windows, imitation brickwork on lower part of house. Height 25¾ ins., length 30 ins.

DOLLS' HOUSE

3144

No. 92. Larger model. Five rooms, including bath room with dummy bath, kitchen with dummy sink, gas stove and dresser. Fitted with four electric wall lights and dummy fireplaces. All windows have metal frames. Garage adjoining has opening doors and the front of the dolls' house is hinged to open in three places. Height 25¾ ins., length 43 ins.

DOLLS' HOUSE

3145

No. 93. A full-sized house of **fashionable Tudor design.** Half-timbered gables and front built-in garage with opening doors. Two bedrooms, dining room, bathroom and kitchen with stove, dresser and sink, staircase and landing. Front opens in four pieces. Side entrance with porch and seat. Opening metal-framed windows with imitation green shutters. Fireplaces in all rooms. Red-tiled roof. Steps and dummy shrubs. Imitation flowered front. Four electric wall lights with switches. Height 27 ins.

L.B.L. PRINCESS ELIZABETH'S DOLLS' HOUSE

L.B.L. Nº 80

PRINCESS ELIZABETH'S DOLLS' HOUSE

3146
A model of the dolls' house presented to Princess Elizabeth by the Welsh people. Double-fronted, with four rooms, hall, staircase and landing. Opening metal windows. Imitation thatched roof. Four electric lights, less batteries. Front hinged in two parts.   Length 30".   Height 23¾".

3147
No. 2. (Not illustrated.) Larger model. Four rooms. Five electric lights. Bathroom with dummy bath, kitchen with dummy sink and gas stove. Garage with opening doors. Otherwise similar to No. 1. Length 47½". Height 31½".

3148
DH 80. Design of a picturesque country residence. Front hinged to open. Six rooms and a hall, fitted with seven electric lights, batteries not included.   All windows and doors open.

> BATTERIES ARE NOT INCLUDED IN THESE MODELS

Transformers can be obtained for working all Dolls' Houses with electric lights from the mains. A.C. only.

3150
DH/12. Six rooms, including fitted bathroom. Curtains to all rooms, dresser, sink, staircase and landing. Fireplaces, etc. Front opens in two pieces. Imitation rough cast and red brick finish. Eight electric lights, less batteries. Now fitted with windows to open.

3149
DH/10. Imitation thatched roof. Opening metal windows, five electric lights, less batteries. Front opens in two pieces. Staircase and landing. Four rooms. Fitted with fireplaces and curtains.

Page Sixty-three

L.B.Ltd.SH/1.

PLAYHOUSES
3151

No. 1. As illustrated. Red brick and imitation white rough cast walls. Green folding shutters. Three pieces.

Models	No. 1	No. 2	No. 3
Height	48	60	64
Width	36	42	45
Depth	37	43	42
	lbs.	lbs.	lbs.
Weight	47½	78	108

No. 3 PLAYHOUSE GARDEN
3152

(not illustrated)

White fence with lych-gate. Awning to fix on house included. Kennel and dovecote. Dimensions given are of garden only. Height taken to top of lych-gate roof. Folds to pack in small space.

Length	...	...	... 72 ins.
Width	...	...	... 46 ins.
Height	...	...	... 43½ ins.
Weight	...	...	... 33 lbs.

SCREEN SHOP
3153

Hinged to take apart in three pieces. Awning on folding tubular frame. Glass windows. Lock and key on door, knocker and letter box. Folding counter inside. Loaves, cakes and basket, as shown, can be supplied at extra cost. Measurements are taken without awning.

Screen Shop			
Height	...	...	54 ins.
Width	...	...	31 ins.
Depth	...	...	48 ins.
Weight	...	...	63½ lbs.

L.B.Ltd
SCREEN SHOP

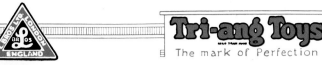
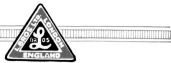

Tri-ang GYRO-CYCLE
AND
Tri-ang GYRO-TRICYCLE

British Patent 479430. Patent Pending in other Countries.
3819 TRI-ANG GYRO-CYCLE

This ingenious scientific toy depends for its action on the well-known gyroscope principle. The gyroscope is built into the front wheel and drives the latter through a train of precision gears. The Gyro-Cycle is an amusingly clever toy and is set in motion by winding a cord round the projecting hub of the front wheel and pulling smartly away. The gay little figure astride the saddle appears to balance himself as he pedals along, and with his flexible arms creates the illusion in the most realistic way that he is steering the Gyro-Cycle by the handlebars. The Gyro-Cycle will run anywhere and is easily demonstrated in a small space. Length 8¼″. Packed in an attractive box, complete with bottle of lubricant oil and spare cords.

Patent Pending.
3820 TRI-ANG GYRO-TRICYCLE

The Gyro-Tricycle is an outstanding novelty with many new tricks. Fitted with gyroscope in front wheel on similar principle to the famous Gyro-Cycle. Packed in attractive box, complete with lubricant and spare cords.

TRI-ANG E.R.A. No. 8
3648

Realistic racing car. Coachbuilt body, aluminium finish, upholstered seat and padded back-rest. Metal exhaust manifold. Crank drive. **Ball-bearing** back axle. Tangent spoke wheels, red enamelled rims, 12″ × 2¼″ Dunlop pneumatic tyres. Klakker horn. Length 49″.

TRI-ANG E.R.A. No 6
3647

Exactly as above, but 11½″ × 1½″ jointless sponge rubber tyres.

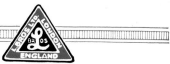
SLEDGES

WOODEN SLEDGES

3743

Stoutly constructed from hardwood and fitted with steel shoes.
Supplied complete with pulling ropes.
No. I. Length 36″.
No. 2 (illus.). Length 48″.

No. 3 TUBULAR SLEDGE

3744

Tubular steel frame, stove enamelled. Wooden seat and
footrest, cellulose enamelled in colour. Supplied complete
with pulling ropes. Length 36″.

TRI-ANG FRONT WHEEL DRIVE TRICYCLES

(Regd.)

TRI-ANG JUNIOR TRICYCLES   SERIES No. 700B

Three sizes 700B, 701B, 702B.

3747

Best quality British cycle tube frames and forks. Nickel-plated handlebars and cranks.
Steps on rear axle. Mudguard on front wheel. Enamelled rims and hubs to wheels.
Sponge rubber tyres. Three sizes. **700.** Front wheel 12″dia. rim, 14″×1″ tyre; rear
wheels 7″ dia. rim, 8½″×1″ tyres. **701.** Front wheel 14″ dia. rim, 16″×1″ tyre; rear
wheels 8½″ dia. rim, 10½″×1″ tyres. **702.** Front wheel 16″ dia. rim, 18″×1¼″ tyre;
rear wheels 10″ dia. rim, 12″×1″ tyres.

TRI-ANG JUNIOR TRICYCLES   SERIES No. 700BB

Three sizes 700BB, 701BB, 702BB.

3748

Best quality British cycle tube frames and forks, **BALL-BEARING** pedals and front
wheel, **CHROMIUM-PLATED** handlebars and wheel rims and hubs. Dunlop two-
coil spring saddle. Sponge rubber tyres. Wheel and tyre sizes as on Series No. 700B.

TRI-ANG JUNIOR TRICYCLES   400 SERIES

Three sizes: Nos. 400, 401 and 402. Diameter of front wheel rims 11″, 13″ and 15″.
Diameter of back wheel rims 7″, 8½″ and 10″. Cycle tube frames. Tangent spoke
wheels, ⅞″ ribbed cushion tyres. Nickel-plated fittings, rubber pedals and handle
grips. Series 400B, 401B and 402B have 1″ cushion tyres. 3746

TRICYCLE TRAILER

TRICYCLE TRAILER

3749

Can easily be fitted to any **TRI-ANG CHAIN DRIVEN TRICYCLE OR TRI-ANG
FRONT WHEEL DRIVE TRICYCLES FROM No. 400 UPWARDS.**
Strongly constructed, the box is finished red and measures 18″×14″×5¼″. The undercarriage is all tubular steel and 13″×1¼″ tangent spoke wheels with jointless sponge
rubber tyres are fitted.

MINIC ALL TO SCALE CLOCKWORK TOYS

Almost every type of vehicle on the road represented ; **some with electric lights.** Strongly constructed, and fitted with powerful, long-running mechanism, and disc wheels with rubber tyres, they will run anywhere, **even on the carpet.** Each model is beautifully finished in a variety of colours, and packed singly in an attractive box. Various quantities according to type are packed in strong outer fibre cases for transit.

20M **MINIC** Light Tank. Length 3¼".

2M **MINIC** Ford Light Van. Length 3⅝".

3M **MINIC** Ford Royal Mail Van. Length 3⅝".

1M **MINIC** Ford £100 Saloon. Length 3½".

7M **MINIC** Town Coupé. Length 4¼".

11M **MINIC** Tractor. Length 3".

18M **MINIC** Vauxhall Town Coupé.

17M **MINIC** Vauxhall Tourer.

19M **MINIC** Vauxhall Cabriolet

6M **MINIC** Cabriolet. Length 4⅜".

8M **MINIC** Open Touring Car. Length 4⅜".

44M **MINIC** Traction Engine. Length 4⅜".

4M **MINIC** Sports Saloon. Length 4⅜".

5M **MINIC** Limousine. Length 4⅜".

10M **MINIC** Delivery Lorry. Length 5½".

52ME **MINIC** Fire Engine with electric head-lamps and battery. Length 6¼".

12M **MINIC** Learner's Car. Length 4⅝".

23M **MINIC** Tip Lorry. Length 5½".

49ME **MINIC** Searchlight Lorry with electric searchlight and battery. Length 5¼".

13M **MINIC** Racing Car. Length 5½".

40M **MINIC** Mechanical Horse and Trailer with cases. Length 7⅜".

48M **MINIC** Breakdown Lorry with Mechanical Crane. Length 5½".

32M **MINIC** Dust Cart. Length 5½".

76M **MINIC** Balloon Barrage Wagon and Trailer. Length 9½"

MINIC Single-deck 'Bus. Length 7¼".
Red 52M   Green 53M

59ME **MINIC** Caravan Set (Tourer with passengers and Caravan, with electric light and battery). Overall length 9⅝".
41ME **MINIC** Caravan with electric light and battery. Length 4¼".

MINIC
Double-deck 'Bus. Length 7¼".
Red 60M   Green 61M

MINIC
38M Caravan Set (non-electric). Overall length 9
16M Caravan (non-electric). Length 4¼".

67

74M **MINIC** Log Lorry. Length 8″

73M **MINIC** Cable Lorry. Length 8¼″.

77M **MINIC** Double-deck Trolley 'Bus. Length 7″.

71M **MINIC** Mechanical Horse and Milk Tanker. Length 7″.

54M Traction Engine and Trailer. Length 8¼″

70M **MINIC** Coal Lorry. Length 6″.

68M **MINIC** Timber Lorry. Length 5¼″.

66M **MINIC** Six-whee Army Lorry. Length 5¼″.

24M **MINIC** Luton Transport Van. Length 5½″.

15M **MINIC** Petrol Tank Lorry. Length 5¾″.

33M **MINIC** Steam Roller. Length 5¼″.

72M **MINIC** Mechanical Horse and Lorry with barrels.

22M **MINIC** C. P. & Co. Van. Length 5½″

25M **MINIC** Delivery Lorry with cases. Length 5½″.

21M **MINIC** Tri-ang Transport Van. Length 5½″.

67M **MINIC** Farm Lorry. Length 5¼″.

SHELL BP FUEL OIL

26M **MINIC** Tractor and Trailer with cases. Length 7¼″.

31M **MINIC** Mechanical Horse and Fuel Oil Trailer. Length 7″.

69M **MINIC** Canvas Tilt Lorry. Length 5½″.

30M **MINIC** Mechanical Horse and Pantechnicon. Length 7⅞″.

75M **MINIC** Ambulance. Length 5⅝″.

39M **MINIC** Taxi. Length 4¼″.

MINIC
50ME Rolls type Sedanca. With electric headlamps and battery. Length 5″.
42M Rolls type Sedanca. (Non-electric.)

55ME **MINIC** Bentley type Tourer with electric headlamps and battery. Length 5¼″.
37M Bentley-type Tourer. (Non-electric.)

MINIC
58ME Daimler type Sunshine Saloon, with electric headlamps and battery. Length 5¼″.
46M Daimler type Sunshine Saloon. (Non-electric.

36M **MINIC** Daimler type Tourer. (Non-electric.) Length 5¼″.

35M **MINIC** Rolls type Tourer. (Non-electric.) Length 5″.

14M **MINIC** Streamline Sports. Length 5″.

34M Tourer with Passengers.

9M **MINIC** Streamline Saloon. Length 5″

56ME **MINIC** Rolls type Sunshine Saloon, with electric headlamps and battery. Length 5¼″.
47M Rolls type Sunshine Saloon. (Non-electric.)

MINIC
51ME Daimler type Sedanca. With electric headlamps and battery. Length 5¼″.
43M Daimler type Sedanca. (Non-electric.)

57ME **MINIC** Bentley type Sunshine Saloon, with electric headlamps and battery. Length 5¼″.
45M Bentley type Sunshine Saloon. (Non-electric.)

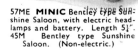

29M **MINIC** Traffic Control Car. Length 5″.

THE ORIGINAL and WORLD RENOWNED

FROG

MK IV FLYING SCALE MODEL AEROPLANES

TRADE MARK REGD.

"FROG" MODEL AIRCRAFT ARE COVERED BY WORLD PATENTS GRANTED AND PENDING

3154

PRICE 5/- COMPLETE

Specification

All metal fuselage of tubular construction, spring steel under-carriage, hollow wings, with patent quick detachable fittings. Powerful motor coupled to a precision cut gearbox, scientifically moulded airscrew. Complete equipment includes fully illustrated flying manual, **Patent High-Speed Winder-Box**, motor lubricant, gearbox oil, two spare motors and insertor rod. Wing Span 11½". Length of flight approximately 300ft.

Spare parts for all models readily obtainable.

RISES OFF THE GROUND.

Everybody should own a "Frog" MK IV—the first and finest Flying-Scale-Model-Aeroplane. The Streamline fuselage is very similar to the new R.A.F. high-speed aircraft. If the model flies into an obstruction or makes an uneven landing, the patent fittings allow for instantaneous detachment of the wings, etc., preventing any serious damage. It is easy to make a "FROG" model perform aerobatics such as a loop, half or flick rolls and numerous other fascinating tricks. There are eight colourful models from which to choose, each with correct national markings and complete with patent HIGH-SPEED WINDER-BOX.

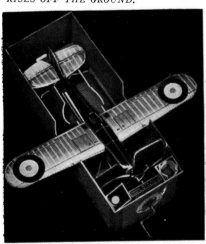

WITH PATENT HIGH SPEED WINDER BOX

"FROG" HANGARS

Two sizes, Nos. 1 and 2. Specially designed for the Frog Mark IV, Hawker Hart and Puss Moth. Complete with double folding-doors, glazed windows, and wind stocking. Finished grey.

DECORATE YOUR "FROG" MODELS

3157

Easily applied transfers in full colours, of the markings and Insignias of famous R.A.F. Squadrons can be obtained. Get a set to-day. Price 1/6.

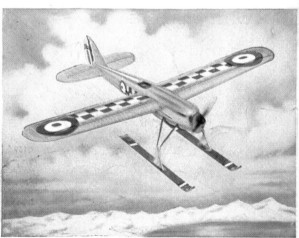

3156

"FROG" SKI-PLANE

Similar to Frog MK IV but fitted with Polished Wood Skis. This undercarriage enables the machine to put up remarkable performances. Attractively finished as shown in the illustration above. A set of Squadron Markings in full service colours is included. Price complete with PATENT HIGH-SPEED WINDER-BOX 7/6. Wing span 11½". Flies 300ft.

7/6

FROG ACE

FROG PILOT

JOIN THE "FROG" CLUB

All owners of "FROG" model Aircraft should become members. NO ENTRANCE FEE. Handsome Enamel Badges, price 6d. each, can be obtained when the simple proficiency tests are passed. Write for details.

ARGENTINE

U.S.A.

ITALY

BELGIUM

FRANCE

HOLLAND

SWEDEN

PERFECT CONSTRUCTION GIVES WONDERFUL PERFORMANCE

AERODYNAMIC ACCURACY

HAWKER HART MARK II DAY BOMBER
ONLY FLYING SCALE MODEL BIPLANE IN THE WORLD

Actual reproduction of the famous R.A.F. High Speed Day Bomber. Real aircraft-type construction with all the details of this famous machine faithfully reproduced. Wing structure of hollow construction with internal supporting ribs, streamline metal struts and bracing wires. Both wing assemblies attached to fuselage by ingenious patent quick-detachable fittings. Telescopic undercarriage and High Power Triple Motor coupled to step-up gearbox.

WILL FLY 750 FT. AT ONE WINDING WITH EXPERIENCE

PRICE
42/-
COMPLETE

SPECIFICATION

Complete equipment includes strong container-box fitted with PATENT HIGH SPEED WINDER, one set of spare motors, lubricant and gearbox oil, triple insertor rod and fully illustrated Flying Manual.

3158

WILL FLY
600 FEET
WITH PRACTICE

Patent high speed winder box supplied with these models.

3159

The "FROG" MAIL PLANE

A model of the very modern high speed freight carrying monoplane, specially designed for carrying mails. Fitted with the famous "Frog" patent detachable wings, a sprung steel "Dowty Type" undercarriage, aluminium spats over the wheels, and typical modern pilot's celluloid cabin. The aeroplane is finished in the official air mail colours with the correct insignia and badges. It flies 600 feet and has a duration of about 30 seconds, and is as nearly as possible crash proof. The undercarriage is not detachable but folds back in a really bad landing.
Fitted with twin elastic motors and step-up twin gear-box (3.4 : 1). Span 18". Complete with Patent High Speed Winder Box.

PRICE
12/6
COMPLETE

3160

The PUSS MOTH

An exceptionally fine Flying-Scale-Model, with all-metal tubular fuselage with strengthening bulkheads. Fitted with transparent windows. Quickly detachable hollow wings with internal supporting ribs and streamline struts. Powerful dual motor with step-up gearbox. Adjustable controls. Patent High Speed Winder Box, motor lubricant, gearbox oil, spare motors, dual inserter rod and fully illustrated flying manual. Wing span 18½". With practice it will rise off the ground and fly 600 feet.

PRICE
15/-
COMPLETE

SUPERB FLYING SCALE MODELS

THE WORLD BEATER!

"FROG" WAKEFIELD TROPHY WINNER

When the team of model aeroplane constructors went to America recently, this model won for England the Wakefield Cup. During one of its flights it remained in the air over eight minutes.

International Model Aircraft, Ltd., realising that many enthusiasts would like to possess a similar model, purchased the exclusive World rights and arranged to manufacture it as a Super Construction kit, under the personal supervision of its designer.

Every wood part in this Kit is shaped out ready to fit together, every wire part is formed to shape; the airscrew is carved out, requiring finishing only, and the famous free-wheel and rubber tensioner device are supplied complete. Full size drawings are, of course, included.

The Wakefield Trophy recently won by Mr. Judge, the designer-pilot of the winning model.

PRICE 21/- COMPLETE KIT OF PARTS

3162

This shows the complete Kit of parts of the Wakefield Trophy model.

3163a
MADE-UP "FROG" COMPETITION MODEL

Obtainable in gold and green or transparent material and green.

PRICE 49/6 COMPLETE

"FROG" COMPETITION MODEL

This "Frog" High-Performance Model conforms to the S.M.A.E. formula and is eligible for official competitions. It has a maximum power duration of 90 seconds, but because of the efficient design and low wing loading, it will fly for much longer periods. When the elastic motor is unwound the combined free-wheeling and tensioner device allows the propeller to idle and at the same time prevents the elastic becoming loose enough to upset the centre of gravity. The elastic motor is enclosed in a balsa-wood cylinder, a unique feature which serves the double purpose of stiffening the fuselage and protecting it in case of a motor breakage.

Wing Span 38". Weight 4 oz. Wing Loading 3.87 oz per sq. foot

PRICE 15/- COMPLETE KIT OF PARTS

3163

FROG TRADE MARK REGD.

FROG KITS FOR THE AERONAUTICAL ENTHUSIAST

These Frog "Penguin" Non-Flying Scale Models are made to such accurate actual aeroplane. Not only in appearance are they like the real thing b results if tested in a wind-tunnel. The completed models are finished in correctly shaped—it only being necessary to fit them together—full except for finishing the hull of the Shor

THE AVRO 504K

3168

The Avro 504K 2-seat Training Biplane has been accurately reproduced in this model as a special Coronation issue. It was in one of these aeroplanes that H.M. the King earned his "wings" as did every fully qualified pilot during the Great War.

4/-

MADE-UP MODEL
7/6

THE PERCIVAL GULL

3164

The Percival Gull Low-wing Cabin "Light Aeroplane" complete with 'glass' cabin, seats, instrument board, registration letters and is exactly to scale in every particular. In turquoise blue and silver, the colours of the "Gull" that won the 1935 King's Cup.

3/-

MADE-UP MODEL 5/-

THE AIRSPEED ENVOY

3170

A fine model of the Airspeed "Envoy," Series II, so well known for its comfort and speed. The model is fitted with chairs, celluloid cabin, metal airscrews, etc., and is available in the following colours: Dark green, emerald green, cream, green / silver and blue.

6/-

MADE-UP MODEL 12/6

THE SINGAPOR

31

This is a really wonderful scale-model of the Short R.3 can be put together by anyone, but the greater care t sufficiently exact to scale to be used for wind-tunnel Guns, bomb-racks, bombs, oil-coolers, exhaust ma control levers, bracing wires, anchor, bollards, cleats, t perfectly made, are supplied with the full Kit of exte AS WITH THE WHOLE "PENGUIN" RANG AVAILABLE.

HANG 31

As soon as you have built your fi structions to build this Hangar. Tru It will hold a large number of them but are obtainable at extra cost.

3167

The Armstrong-Whitworth A.W.35 "Scimitar" Single Seat Fighter. An excellent model of the high performance two-gun fighting biplane. Supplied with Chinese (Kangszi), or Norwegian insignia and colours. The usual complete equipment is provided.

4/-

THE SCIMITAR

MADE-UP MODEL 7/6

it is almost impossible to tell a photograph of a model from one of the
details as the cross-section of struts, etc. The models would give correct
ct colours and markings and the construction kits include all parts
wings, cements, paints, etc., and no tools whatsoever are required
pore III " which is only partly shaped.

THE BLACKBURN SHARK

3169

A fine model of the Black-
burn "Shark," the largest
land-going Aeroplane of the
Fleet Air Arm. The com-
plete Kit of Parts includes
engine, cowl, airscrew, exhaust, manifolds, gun-ring,
cockpit, deck, torpedo, etc.,
paints and transfers for
finishing.

LYING BOAT

ore III 4-engine Flying Boat. The model
ore beautiful is the finished result. It is

ter header-tanks, petrol gravity-tanks,
le, boat hook, drogues, scuttles, etc., all

ETELY FINISHED MODELS ARE

15/-

MADE-UP MODEL

63/-

5/6

MADE-UP MODELS
12/6

THE DIANA

3171

" The Aeroplane that revo-
lutionised Air Transport " is
the de Havilland 86A
4-engine " Diana " Biplane,
which is faithfully reproduced in this model. It is
fully equipped with chairs,
etc., and is obtainable in
the following colours :—
Dark green, emerald green,
cream, green/silver and blue.

7/6

MADE-UP MODEL 15/-

KIT

obtain the parts and in-
ith all "Penguin" Aircraft.
and trolley not included,

7/6

This illustration shows
the full Kit of parts in a
strong cardboard box
with all the photo-
graphs, charts, etc.,
necessary to build a
Scale-model.

THE GLOSTER GLADIATOR

3166

A perfect scale model of the
" Gloster " Gladiator, the
extreme super-performance
fighter of the Royal Air
Force.
With the help of the chart
and full instructions it is
only a matter of careful
assembly to have a really
fine model.

3/6

MADE-UP MODEL

6/6

3165

The world-famous all-metal
fighting machine can be
perfectly made from the full
Kit, including cement,
paint, transfers, etc. The
enthusiasts who follow the
instructions carefully will be
well repaid with a really
beautiful scale-model of the
Hawker Fury.

THE HAWKER FURY

3/-

MADE-UP MODEL 5/6

The AVENGER
3175

Built on the same new principle as the Raider, this model is unusually strong with its tubular fuselage, spring undercarriage, balsa wood wings. Both models are finished in the R.A.F. colours. Can be flown both indoors and out of doors. Wing Span 11″.

PRICE 1/-

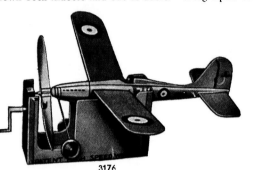

3176

FLIES NEARLY 200 FEET UNDER GOOD CONDITIONS

AVENGER
Boxed complete with Patent High-Speed Winder

1/11

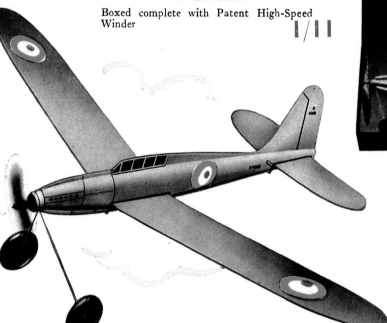

A FLYING MODEL OF THE LATEST TYPE BOMBER IN THE R.A.F.

The 'RAIDER'

HIGH-SPEED WINDER

RAIDER
Boxed complete with Patent High-Speed Winder

2/11

3178

The RAIDER
3177

PRICE 1/11

Here is a wonderful new model within the reach of every boy's pocket. It is modelled on the lines of the R.A.F. High Speed Dive Bombers. It is almost unbreakable as an entirely new method of manufacture is used. Exceptional performance. Wing Span 13¼″.

The BANTAM

A splendid model which flies any-where. Attractive appearance and excellent performance.
Wing span 9″. Complete with PATENT HIGH-SPEED WINDER-BOX, spare motor and lubricant.

2/6

3180

The TADPOLE

Amazing flights in any room, large or small. Duration 30 seconds. Wing span 8″. Quickly wound with PATENT HIGH-SPEED WINDER-BOX.

2/6

These are the high speed winder boxes supplied with the Bantam and Tadpole models.

3179

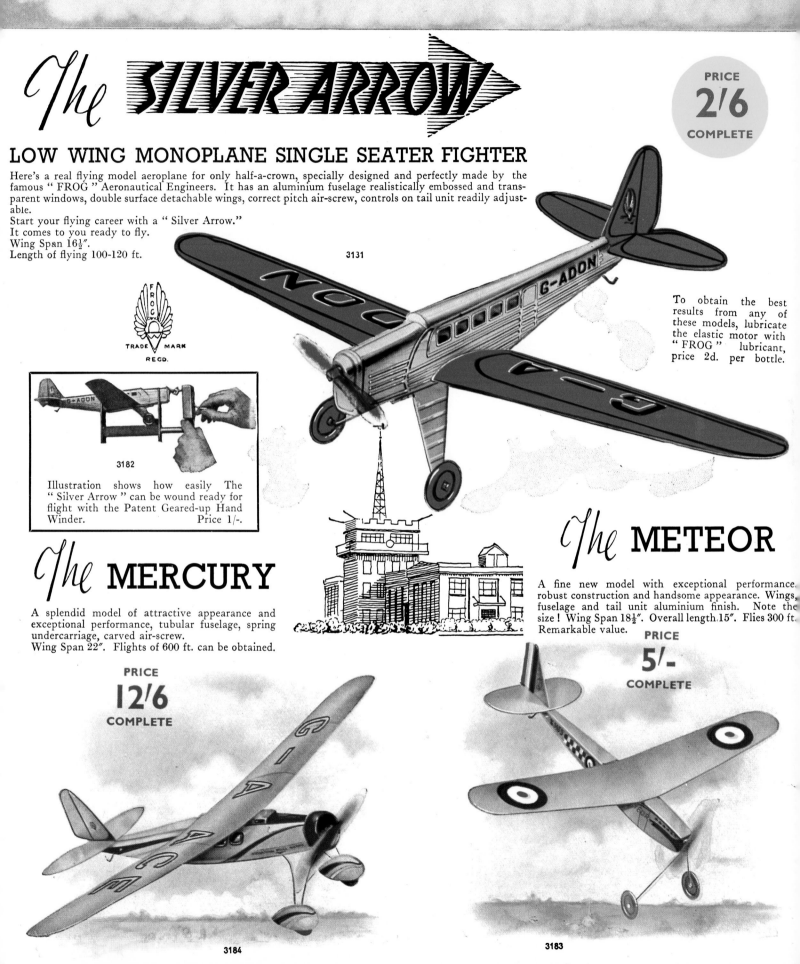

The SILVER ARROW →

LOW WING MONOPLANE SINGLE SEATER FIGHTER

Here's a real flying model aeroplane for only half-a-crown, specially designed and perfectly made by the famous " FROG " Aeronautical Engineers. It has an aluminium fuselage realistically embossed and transparent windows, double surface detachable wings, correct pitch air-screw, controls on tail unit readily adjustable.

Start your flying career with a " Silver Arrow."
It comes to you ready to fly.
Wing Span 16½".
Length of flying 100-120 ft.

3131

To obtain the best results from any of these models, lubricate the elastic motor with " FROG " lubricant, price 2d. per bottle.

3182

Illustration shows how easily The " Silver Arrow " can be wound ready for flight with the Patent Geared-up Hand Winder.   Price 1/-.

The MERCURY

A splendid model of attractive appearance and exceptional performance, tubular fuselage, spring undercarriage, carved air-screw.
Wing Span 22". Flights of 600 ft. can be obtained.

PRICE 12/6 COMPLETE

The METEOR

A fine new model with exceptional performance, robust construction and handsome appearance. Wings, fuselage and tail unit aluminium finish. Note the size ! Wing Span 18½". Overall length 15". Flies 300 ft. Remarkable value.

PRICE 5/- COMPLETE

3184

3183

NO TOOLS REQUIRED. ALL PARTS CUT TO SHAPE.

"FROG" FLYING CONSTRUCTION KITS
FLYING SCALE MODELS OF FAMOUS CIVIL AND MILITARY AIRCRAFT

The now famous series of Constructional Kits, with one additional Kit (the New Model Fairey III F) is shown on this page. All parts are accurately cut to shape and only need assembling, covering and gluing together. Each kit is complete and everything is supplied for the construction of the finished model, all wire parts being bent to shape.

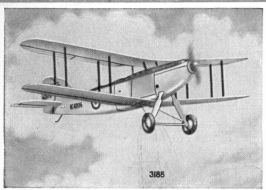

NEW MODEL FAIREY III F

5/6

A flying model of one of the most famous aeroplanes in the R.A.F. which has been flown all over the World for 10 years and is still in service. The kit includes carved wood airscrew, wing assembly jig, full scale drawings and instructions, glue, silver paint, service transfers, etc. Exceptionally fine performance. Span 15"

THE DE HAVILLAND LEOPARD MOTH

2/6

An easily assembled model of the popular civil aeroplane. A fully illustrated step-by-step instruction sheet is included which makes assembly of the accurately made parts a simple matter. Wing span 12¾"

THE DE HAVILLAND HORNET MOTH

3/6

A really splendid model, everything cut to shape ready to assemble. The finished model has an extremely handsome appearance and really good performance. Wing span 11¼"

This illustration shows the contents of the complete kit of the de Havilland Hornet Moth and shows how all the important parts are already accurately cut to shape. All "FROG" Constructional Kits are absolutely complete with ample quantities of tissue, cement and dope. Only the finest quality materials are included, thus ensuring the maximum strength and rigidity to the completed model.

3186

THE MILES HAWK-MAJOR CONSTRUCTION KIT

A Constructional Kit for the more advanced model maker. Complete with all fuselage sides, bulkheads, wing ribs, wing tips, spars, fairing-pieces, tailplane ribs, rudder and fin, undercarriage legs, etc.
ALL CUT TO SHAPE.

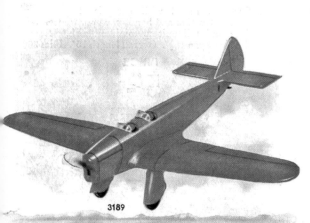

3189

The kit includes a finished, carved air screw, step-up gearbox and aluminium wheels, together with sufficient dope, cement and special colours. When complete it is a particularly attractive model of this famous High Speed Monoplane. An easy-to-follow illustrated instruction sheet with full size drawings and photographs is supplied with each kit.

Wing Span 16½". With a little experience flights of 600 ft. are obtainable.

10/6

3187

THE HAWKER DEMON

4/6

Build this splendid model of the Hawker Demon, the famous 2-seater Service Aeroplane. All parts are made ready to assemble. Special light wheels are included. Wing span 12¼"

3190

UNIVERSAL HAND WINDERS !
A Constructional Kit is available for building a geared-up Universal Hand Winder for use with "FROG" Scale Model Construction Kits or any "FROG" Model with a propeller not exceeding 5½ ins. diameter. All parts are **cut ready to assemble** and only require gluing together. **GEARED-UP WINDER MECHANISM IS COMPLETELY ASSEMBLED.**

1/-

SOLE CONCESSIONAIRES : LINES BROS. LTD., TRI-ANG WORKS, LONDON, S.W.19
DESIGNED AND MADE IN ENGLAND BY INTERNATIONAL MODEL AIRCRAFT LTD.

Price Key

to

Tri-ang Toys

REGD TRADE MARK

ILLUSTRATED IN THE FOLLOWING SECTIONAL CATALOGUES

Catalogue No. 37   General Toys.

„   No. 37A "Fairycycles," "Tricycles," & Juvenile Cycles.

„   No. 37B "Minic" & "Tri-ang" Clockwork Toys.

„   No. 37C "Frog" Model Aircraft.

JULY 13th, 1936

The finest Toys for Girls or Boys!

LINES BROS. Ltd.

TRI-ANG WORKS, MORDEN RD., LONDON, S.W.19

Telephone : LIBerty 4242 (6 Lines)
Telegrams : TRIANGTOIS, 'PHONE LONDON
Code : WESTERN UNION (5 Letter)

Manchester Branch :
WERNETH GOODS STATION
MIDDLETON ROAD, OLDHAM

'Phone :
OLDHAM MAIN 2484 and 2485

City Showrooms :
18, New Union Street, London, E.C.2
'Phone : METropolitan 0337

UNIQUE & UNITY CYCLE
Co., Ltd.
(Prop. : Lines Bros. Ltd.),
CAMP LANE, HANDSWORTH
BIRMINGHAM
'Phone : ASTON CROSS 3588-9

Page in Illustrated List	Index Reference No.	ARTICLE.	Price.	Maintained Advtd. Retail Selling Price
		CHILDREN'S CARS.		
1	2115	**Crown,** 6″ spoke wheels, $\frac{7}{16}$″ tyres ...	8/6	
	2116	**Prince,** 6″ disc „ $\frac{1}{2}$″ „ ...	9/-	
	2117	**Jubilee,** 6″ „ „ $\frac{3}{4}$″ „ ...	14/-	10/6
2	2118	**Lizzie,** 6″ „ „ $\frac{1}{2}$″ „ ...	19/-	
	2119	**Bentley,** 6″ „ „ $\frac{1}{2}$″ „ ...	24/6	
	2120	**Mitcham,** 8″ balloon „ $\frac{1}{2}$″ „ ...	29/-	
3	2121	**Vauxhall Tourer,** 8″ balloon wheels, $\frac{1}{2}$″ tyres	30/-	22/6
	2122	**Vauxhall Special,** $8\frac{1}{2}$″ tangent spoke wheels, 1″ cushion tyres ...	36/8	27/6
	2123	**Imp,** 9″ disc wheels, $\frac{5}{8}$″ tyres ...	33/4	25/-
4	2124	**Chevrolet Regal,** 9″ balloon wheels, $\frac{5}{8}$″ tyres, BALL BEARING BACK AXLE	39/4	
	2125	**Tri-ang Sports,** 8″ balloon wheels, $\frac{1}{2}$″ tyres	43/4	32/6
	2126	**Swift,** 9″ balloon wheels, $\frac{5}{8}$″ tyres, BALL BEARING BACK AXLE	50/-	37/6
5	2127	**Tri-ang Special,** 8″ tangent spoke wheels, 1″ cushion tyres ...	56/-	42/-
	2128	**Humber,** 9″ balloon wheels, $\frac{5}{8}$″ tyres, BALL BEARING BACK AXLE	56/-	42/-
	2129	**Buick Regal,** 10″ tangent spoke wheels, $1\frac{1}{16}$″ Auto tread tyres ...	66/-	49/6
6	2130	**Epoch,** 9″ balloon wheels, $\frac{5}{8}$″ tyres, BALL BEARING BACK AXLE	66/-	49/6
	2131	**Streamline,** 9″ balloon wheels, $\frac{5}{8}$″ tyres, BALL BEARING BACK AXLE	73/4	55/-
	2132	**Tri-ang de Luxe,** $8\frac{1}{2}$″ tangent spoke wheels, $1\frac{1}{4}$″ jointless sponge tyres	79/4	59/6
7	2133	**Sceptre,** 10″ tangent spoke wheels, $1\frac{1}{8}$″ sponge tyres, CHAIN & CRANK DRIVE, 2 ELECTRIC LIGHTS, less battery	112/-	84/-
	2134	**Airflow,** 10″ tangent spoke wheels, $1\frac{1}{8}$″ sponge tyres, CHAIN & CRANK DRIVE, 2 ELECTRIC LIGHTS, less battery	120/-	90/-
	2135	**Vauxhall Majestic No. 8,** $2\frac{1}{4}$″ Dunlop pneumatic tyres, CHAIN & CRANK DRIVE, CHROM. FITTINGS	168/-	126/-
	2136	**Vauxhall Majestic No. 6,** as No. 8 but $1\frac{1}{8}$″ sponge tyres, NICKEL PLATED FITTINGS	120/-	90/-
8	2137	**Magna No. 8,** BALL BEARING BACK AXLE, $2\frac{1}{4}$″ Dunlop pneumatic tyres, CHROM. FITTINGS	153/4	115/-
	2138	**Magna No. 6,** as No. 8 but with $1\frac{1}{8}$″ sponge tyres, NICKEL PLATED FITTINGS	106/-	79/6
	2139	**Greyhound,** BALL BEARING BACK AXLE, $2\frac{1}{4}$″ Dunlop pneumatic tyres	168/-	126/-
	2140	**Two-seater Sports No. 6,** tangent spoke wheels, $1\frac{1}{4}$″ jointless sponge tyres	120/-	90/-
	2141	**Two-seater Sports No. 8,** as No. 6 but with $2\frac{1}{4}$″ Dunlop pneumatic tyres	168/-	126/-
9	2142	**Bentley Racer,** 9″ balloon wheels, $\frac{5}{8}$″ tyres	39/4	29/6
	2143	**Bentley Racer Major,** 11″ balloon wheels, $\frac{5}{8}$″ tyres, BALL BEARING BACK AXLE	52/8	39/6
	2144	**Speedy Racer,** $8\frac{1}{2}$″ tangent spoke wheels, 1″ cushion tyres, ELECTRIC HORN	70/-	52/6
	2145	**Magna Racer No. 8,** BALL BEARING BACK AXLE, aluminium body, $2\frac{1}{4}$″ Dunlop pneumatic tyres	126/8	95/-
	2146	**Magna Racer No. 6,** as No. 8 but with $1\frac{1}{8}$″ sponge tyres	90/-	67/6

Page in Illustrated List	Index Reference No.	ARTICLE.	Price.	Maintained Advtd. Retail Selling Price
		Children's Cars—(contd.).		
10	2147	**Electric Rolls,** 12v. Lucas motor, $2\frac{1}{4}$″ Dunlop pneumatic tyres	840/-	630/-
	2148	**Rolls Royce Type Motor No. 8,** ball bearing double crank action, $2\frac{1}{4}$″ Dunlop Pneumatic tyres	280/-	210/-
11	2149	**Crown Tip Lorry,** 6″ disc wheels, $\frac{1}{2}$″ tyres	16/8	12/6
	2150	**Chevrolet Tip Lorry,** 9″ balloon wheels, $\frac{5}{8}$″ tyres	50/-	37/6
	2151	**Big Tip Lorry,** 11″ balloon wheels, $\frac{5}{8}$″ tyres	112/-	84/-
12	2152	**Pedal Loco,** 9″ balloon wheels, $\frac{5}{8}$″ tyres	66/-	49/6
		EXTRAS ON MOTORS.		
		Electric Horn, Rear Light, Direction Indicator, Electric Tell-tale Dash, complete with Batteries	16/8	12/6
		Electric Light	4/-	
		Electric Light, 2 lights on Epoch Streamline, Tri-ang Sports, and Tri-ang Special	6/8	5/-
		PEDAL PLANES.		
	2153	**Taxiplane**	60/-	45/-
	2154	**Transatlantic**	76/8	57/6
		DOLLS PRAMS.		
13	2155	**16/S**	8/6	
	2156	**18/S**	11/-	
	2157	**20/S**	13/-	
	2158b	**16/A,** steel body, 5″ spoke wheels, $\frac{1}{2}$″ tyres (not illustrated)	15/6	
	2158	**16/U.T., steel body,** 5″ spoke wheel, $\frac{1}{2}$″ tyres	19/-	
	2159	**18/U.T.,** steel body, 6″ spoke wheels, $\frac{1}{2}$″ tyres	25/-	
	2160	**18/A,** steel body, 6″ spoke wheels, $\frac{1}{2}$″ tyres	20/-	
	2161	**18/B,** steel body, 6″ spoke wheels, $\frac{1}{2}$″ tyres	25/6	
	2162	**20/B,** steel body, 6″ spoke wheels, $\frac{1}{2}$″ tyres	34/-	
14	2163	**20/W,** steel body, 6″ tangent spoke wheels, $\frac{5}{8}$″ tyres	29/-	
	2164	**22/W,** steel body, 6″ tangent spoke wheels, $\frac{5}{8}$″ tyres	36/8	
	2165	**22/U.T.,** steel body, 6″ tangent spoke wheels, 1″ cushion tyres	45/-	
	2166	**22/C,** steel body, 7″ tangent spoke wheels, 1″ cushion tyres ...	56/-	
	2167	**24/W,** steel body, 7″ tangent spoke wheels, $\frac{5}{8}$″ tyres	42/-	
15	2168	**24/S,** steel body, 7″ tangent spoke wheels, 1″ cushion tyres	50/-	
	2169	**24/X,** wood body, 7″ tangent spoke wheels, 1″ cushion tyres	50/-	
	2170	**24/D,** steel body, 7″ tangent spoke wheels, 1″ cushion tyres	56/-	42/-
	2171	**24/M,** wood body, 7″ tangent spoke wheels, 1″ cushion tyres	66/-	
16	2172	**24/C,** steel body, 7″ tangent spoke wheels, 1″ cushion tyres	73/4	
	2173	**24/K,** wood body, $8\frac{1}{2}$″ tangent spoke wheels, 1″ cushion tyres	73/4	
	2174	**24/U.T.,** steel body, 7″ tangent spoke wheels, 1″ cushion tyres	73/4	
	2175	**26/X,** steel body, 7″ spoke wheels, $\frac{5}{8}$″ cushion tyres	46/8	
17	2176	**26/W,** steel body, 7″ tangent spoke wheels, 1″ cushion tyres	52/8	
	2177	**26/C,** steel body, 7″ tangent spoke wheels, 1″ cushion tyres	73/4	
	2178	**26/T,** steel body, $8\frac{1}{2}$″ tangent spoke wheels, 1″ cushion tyres	106/-	79/6
	2179	**Advance,** wood body, 7″ tangent spoke wheels, 1″ cushion tyres ...	79/4	59/6

Page in Illustrated List	Index Reference No.	ARTICLE.	Price.	Maintained Advtd. Retail Selling Price
		DOLLS FOLDERS		
18	2180	00 D.B.F., 5″ spoke wheels, $\frac{1}{2}$″ tyres	14/6	
	2181	0 „ 6″ „ „ $\frac{1}{2}$″ „	21/-	
	2182	1 „ 6″ „ „ $\frac{5}{8}$″ „	28/-	21/-
	2183	5 „ 6″ „ „ $\frac{5}{8}$″ „	36/8	27/6
	2184	6 „ 6″ „ „ 1″ cushion tyres	50/-	37/6
	2185	D Giant, 6″ spoke wheels, $\frac{1}{2}$″ tyres	26/-	
	2186	0 Sunkar, 5″ „ „ $\frac{3}{8}$″ „	10/6	
	2187	10 „ 6″ tangent spoke wheels, $\frac{5}{8}$″ tyres	20/-	
19	2188	Dot Folder, steel disc wheels ...	2/10	
	2189	Midget Folder, 3″ steel disc wheels, rubber tyres.	4/2	
	2190	Elf Folder, 5″ spoke wheels, $\frac{3}{8}$″ tyres	6/-	
	2191	A Giant, 5″ „ „ $\frac{3}{8}$″ „	10/-	
	2192	C „ 5″ „ „ $\frac{3}{8}$″ „	19/-	
	2193	'O' Sulky, 6″ spoke wheels, $\frac{1}{2}$″ tyres	7/-	5/6
		PEDAL KARS AND TINY TRIKE.		
20	2194	Tiny Trike	8/8	6/6
	2195	Toddletrike	4/-	
	2196	"O" Pedalkar, 4 in a box	4/4	
	2197	1 „ 4 in a box	6/8	
	2198	1B „ 2 in a box	9/-	
	2199	2B „	7/8	
21	2200	4A „	13/-	
	2201	4S „	14/-	10/6
	2202	4B „	14/-	10/6
	2203	4SS „	20/-	15/-
	2204	4XX Special All Chrom.	33/4	25/-
22	2205	40A Safety Pedal Kar	14/-	10/6
	2206	5B	20/8	15/6
	2207	5XX Special All Chrom.	33/4	25/-
	2208	6A Pedal Kar	43/4	32/6
	2209	7 „ „	18/-	13/6
		TODDLEKARS.		
23	2210	B Toddlekar	8/-	
	2211	D „	14/-	10/6
	2212	E „	20/-	15/-
	2213	G „	28/-	21/-
	2214	Tray Rocker	10/-	7/6
24	2215	Gee Gee Kar	28/-	21/-
	2216	Rapid Racer	8/8	6/6
	2217	Dobbin Hand Car	16/8	12/6
		BUILDING BRICKS.		
	2218	Kindergarten Building Bricks, painted	46/8	35/-
	a	Kindergarten Building Bricks, unpainted	23/4	17/6
		SCOOTERS.		
25	2219	O-D Scooter	3/-	
	2220	A „	4/-	
	2221	B „	6/6	
	2222	3 „	7/8	
	2223	C „	10/8	7/11
	2224	F/16 „	10/8	7/11
	2225	D „	12/8	9/6
	2226	F „	20/-	15/-
	2227	G „	23/4	17/6
	2228	F/7 Tri-ang Scoot	26/-	19/6
	2229	F/8 „ „	30/-	22/6
	a	F/8C „ „ SPECIAL ALL CHROM.	50/-	37/6
	2230	F/20 „ „	50/-	37/6
	a	F/20C „ „ SPECIAL ALL CHROM.	66/-	49/6
		STILTS.		
	2231	Stilts	8/-	

Page in Illustrated List	Index Reference No.	ARTICLE.	Price.	Maintained Advtd. Retail Selling Price
		VANS, ETC.		
26	2232	Royal Mail Van	14/-	10/6
	2233	Daily Mail Van	14/-	10/6
	2234	Tri-ang Transport Six	14/-	10/6
	a	„ „ „ 2 electric lights	16/-	12/6
	2235	Tri-ang Transport Van	14/-	10/6
	a	„ „ „ 2 electric lights	16/-	12/6
	2236	Bedford Shell Wagon	5/4	3/11
	2237	„ Breakdown Lorry	5/4	3/11
	2238	„ Tip Lorry	5/4	3/11
	2239	„ Van	5/4	3/11
27	2240	„ Milk Lorry	8/-	5/11
	2241	Metal C.P. & Co. Van	4/10	
	2242	„ Tipping Lorry, 1/T	4/2	
	2243	„ Van, 1/V	4/2	
	2244	„ Breakdown Lorry, 1/BL ...	4/2	
	2245	London Transport Omnibus E ...	20/-	15/6
	2246	„ „ „ No. 2 ...	39/4	29/6
	2247	Tri-ang Transport 4	6/8	4/11
		NON-MECHANICAL STEEL TOYS.		
28	2248	OOO Farm Truck	8d.	6d.
	2249	OO „ „	1/4	1/-
	a	OOE „ „ with elec. light	2/-	1/6
	2250	O „ „	2/-	1/6
	a	OE „ „ with elec. light	2/8	1/11
	2251	OOO Tipping Lorry	8d.	6d.
	2252	OO „ „	1/4	1/-
	a	OOE „ „ with elec. light	2/-	1/6
	2253	O „ „	2/-	1/6
	a	OE „ „ with elec. light	2/8	1/11
	2254	OOO Breakdown Lorry	8d.	6d.
	2255	OO „ „	1/4	1/-
	a	OOE „ „ with elec. light	2/-	1/6
	2256	O „ „	2/-	1/6
	a	OE „ „ with elec. light	2/8	1/11
	2257	OOO Wagon and Horses	8d.	6d.
	2258	OO „ „ „	1/4	1/-
	2259	O „ „ „	2/-	1/6
29	2260	OOO Forward Drive Lorry	8d.	6d.
	2261	OO „ „ „	1/4	1/-
	a	OOE „ „ „ with elec. light	2/-	1/6
	2262	O Forward Drive Lorry	2/-	1/6
	a	OE „ „ „ with elec. light	2/8	1/11
	2263	OOO Steam Rollers	8d.	6d.
	2264	OO „ „	1/4	1/-
	a	OOE „ „ with elec. light	2/-	1/6
	2265	O „ „	2/-	1/6
	a	OE „ „ with elec. light	2/8	1/11
	2266	OOO Traction Engine	8d.	6d.
	2267	OO „ „	1/4	1/-
	a	OOE „ „ with elec. light	2/-	1/6
	2268	O „ „	2/-	1/6
	a	OE „ „ with elec. light	2/8	1/11
	2269	OOO Van	8d.	6d.
	2270	OO Royal Mail Van	1/4	1/-
	a	OOE „ „ „ with elec. light	2/-	1/6
	2271	O „ „ „	2/-	1/6
	a	OE „ „ „ with elec. light	2/8	1/11
	2272	OOO Monoplane	8d.	6d.
30	2273	OOO Coupe	8d.	6d.
	2274	OO „	1/4	1/-
	a	OOE „ with elec. light ...	2/-	1/6
	2275	OOO Racing Car	8d.	6d.
	2276	OO „ „	1/4	1/-
	a	OOE „ „ with elec. light ...	2/-	1/6
	2277	OOO Green Line Coach	8d.	6d.
	2278	OO Sweeper	1/4	1/-
	2279	OOO Crane	8d.	6d.
	2280	OO „	1/4	1/-
	2281	OO Dock Crane	1/4	1/-
	2282	O „ „	2/-	1/6

LARGE CRANES.

Page	Index Ref. No.	ARTICLE	Price	Maintained Advtd Retail Selling Price
31	2283	No. 1 Crane	2/10	
	2284	No. 2 ,,	5/6	3/11
	2285	No. 3 ,,	9/4	6/11
	2286	Dock Crane	5/6	3/11

STEEL FOLDING POLE CART.

Page	Index Ref. No.	ARTICLE	Price	Maintained Advtd Retail Selling Price
	2287	O Steel Folding Pole Cart	2/8	

"K" YACHTS AND TRI-ANG RACING YACHTS.

Page	Index Ref. No.	ARTICLE	Price	Maintained Advtd Retail Selling Price
32	2288	OOO K Dinghy	8d.	6d.
	a	OOO K Yacht	8d.	6d.
	b	OO ,, with steel hulls	1/4	1/-
	c	O ,,	3/4	2/6
	d	1 ,,	4/8	3/6
	2289	K10 Yacht, special finish, steel hull	2/-	1/6
	a	K12 ,, ,, ,,	3/4	2/6
	b	K14 ,, ,, ,,	6/-	4/6
	c	K16 ,, ,, ,,	8/-	5/11
	2290	X ,, patent one-piece hull	10/-	7/6
	a	Y ,, ,, ,, ,,	14/-	10/6
	2291	K2 ,, with automatic steering	20/-	15/-
	a	K3 ,,	30/-	22/6
	b	K4 ,,	43/4	32/6

"K" SPEEDBOATS.

Page	Index Ref. No.	ARTICLE	Price	Maintained Advtd Retail Selling Price
33	2292	OOO Speedboat	1/4	1/-
	a	OO ,,	3/4	2/6
	b	O ,,	6/-	4/6
	c	1 ,,	8/8	6/6
	2293	2C ,,	14/-	10/6
	2294	3C ,,	28/-	21/-
	a	3E ,, electric motor	33/4	25/-
	2295	4C ,,	39/4	29/6
	a	4E ,, electric motor	46/8	35/-
	2296	5E ,,	52/8	39/6
	2297	"A" Tri-ang Electric Cabin Cruiser "Dido"	43/4	32/6
	a	"B" Tri-ang Electric Cabin Cruiser "Juno"	52/8	39/6
	b	"C" Tri-ang Electric Cabin Cruiser "Venus"	66/-	49/6
	2298	"D" Tri-ang Electric Cabin Cruiser "Ariadne"	140/-	105/-

Batteries not included in Speedboats or Cabin Cruisers.

CLOCKWORK COASTAL STEAMERS.

Page	Index Ref. No.	ARTICLE	Price	Maintained Advtd Retail Selling Price
34	2299	No. 1 Coastal Steamer	14/-	10/6
	2300	,, 2 ,, ,,	23/4	17/6
	2301	,, 3 ,, ,,	39/4	29/6

CHILDREN'S PLAYBOATS.

Page	Index Ref. No.	ARTICLE	Price	Maintained Advtd Retail Selling Price
	2302	"A" Playboat, with oars & rowlocks	112/-	84/-
	2303	"B" ,, as "A" but fitted with mast and sail	140/-	105/-
	2304	"C" Playboat, as "B" but fitted with two paddle wheels	173/4	130/-

STANDS FOR DISPLAY OF YACHTS, SPEEDBOATS AND CABIN CRUISERS.

ARTICLE	Price
Yacht Stand to take OOO, OO, O, and 1	5/-
Speedboat Stand to take five numbers from OOO	5/-
Cabin Cruiser Stand to take A, B, and C	5/-

L.M.S. WOOD ENGINES.

Page	Index Ref. No.	ARTICLE	Price	Maintained Advtd Retail Selling Price
35	2305	A, 6 in a box	3/4	2/6
	2306	B, 6 in a box	4/8	3/6
	2307	C, each in a box	6/4	4/9
	2308	D, ,,	8/-	5/11
	2309	E, ,,	14/-	10/6
	2310	F, ,,	20/8	15/6

TRI-ANG LOCOS.

Page	Index Ref. No.	ARTICLE	Price	Maintained Advtd Retail Selling Price
	2311	10, 12 in a box	2/8	
	2312	11, 12 ,,	3/4	
	2313	12, 12 ,,	4/4	
	2314	13, each in a box	5/4	
	2315	14, ,,	6/4	
	2316	15, ,,	7/-	

TRAIN SETS.

Page	Index Ref. No.	ARTICLE	Price	Maintained Advtd Retail Selling Price
36	2317	O Train Set	6/4	
	2318	M ,,	8/-	5/11
	2319	C ,,	16/8	12/6
	2320	E ,,	33/4	25/-

TUG AND BARGE SET.

Page	Index Ref. No.	ARTICLE	Price	Maintained Advtd Retail Selling Price
	2321	Tug and Barge Set	2/8	1/11

ROAD, RIVER AND RAIL SET.

Page	Index Ref. No.	ARTICLE	Price	Maintained Advtd Retail Selling Price
	2322	Road, River and Rail Set	4/-	2/11

PUFF PUFF ENGINES.

Page	Index Ref. No.	ARTICLE	Price	Maintained Advtd Retail Selling Price
37	2323	No. 1 Puff Puff, 4 wheels	14/-	10/6
	2324	No 2 ,, ,, 6 ,,	20/-	15/-

VICTOR ENGINE.

Page	Index Ref. No.	ARTICLE	Price	Maintained Advtd Retail Selling Price
	2325	Victor Engine	39/4	29/6

STEEL PLANES AND STEAM ROLLERS.

Page	Index Ref. No.	ARTICLE	Price	Maintained Advtd Retail Selling Price
	2326	Imperial Airways No. 1, 1 engine	14/-	10/6
	2327	,, ,, No. 2, 3 ,,	18/-	13/6
	2328	No. 1 Steam Roller	12/-	8/11
	2329	No. 2 ,, ,,	16/8	12/6
	2330	No. 3 ,, ,,	20/-	15/-
	2331	No. 4 ,, ,,	30/-	22/6

PUSH HORSES, ROCKING HORSES, HORSES AND CARTS.

Page	Index Ref. No.	ARTICLE	Price	Maintained Advtd Retail Selling Price
38	2332	Stool Horse	5/4	
	2333	Folding Push Horse, Size A	7/4	
	b	,, ,, ,, Size B	12/-	
	2334	Folding Rocking Horse, Size A	6/8	
	b	,, ,, ,, Size B	13/4	
	2335	Roller Rocker	10/-	
	2336	Hollow Push Horse, Size X	8/-	
	b	,, ,, ,, Size Z	13/-	
	2337	Hobby Horses, OO	3/-	
	b	,, ,, O	5/-	
	c	,, ,, 1	7/-	
	d	,, ,, 2	9/-	
39	2338	OOO Pine Carts & Horses, 2 in a box	8/8	6/6
	b	OO Pine Carts & Horses, 2 in a box	10/8	7/11
	c	O ,, ,, ,, ,,	12/8	9/6
	d	1 ,, ,, ,, ,,	16/8	12/6
	e	2 ,, ,, ,, ,,	20/8	15/6
	f	3 ,, ,, ,, ,,	24/8	18/6
	2339	No. 1 Elm Tip Carts & Horses	15/-	22/6
	b	,, 2 ,, ,, ,,	39/4	29/6
	c	,, 3 ,, ,, ,,	50/-	37/6
	d	,, 4 ,, ,, ,,	70/-	52/6
	e	,, 5 ,, ,, ,,	96/-	72/6
	f	,, 6 ,, ,, ,,	130/-	97/6
	2340	Tubular Rocker	20/-	15/-
	2341	Old Style Rocking Horse	26/-	19/6

Page in Illustrated List	Index Reference No.	ARTICLE	Price	Maintained Advtd Retail Selling Price	Page in Illustrated List	Index Reference No.	ARTICLE	Price	Maintained Advtd Retail Selling Price
		Push Horses & Rocking Horses (contd.)				2363	Elm Barrow 1	10/-	7/6
	2342	No. 1 Push Horse	14/-	10/6		b	„ „ 2	14/-	10/6
	b	„ 2 „ „	20/-	15/-		c	„ „ 3	18/-	13/6
	c	„ 3 „ „	28/-	21/-		d	„ „ 4	22/-	16/6
	d	„ 4 „ „	39/4	29/6		e	„ „ 5	26/-	19/6
	e	„ 5 „ „	50/-	37/6		2364	Steel Barrow OO, packed 6 in a carton	3/4	
40	f	„ 6 „ „	80/-	60/-		b	Steel Barrow O, packed 6 in a carton	5/-	
	2343	"Sportiboy" Safety Rocking Horse, No. 1	66/-	49/6		c	„ „ 1, „ „	6/8	
	b	"Sportiboy" Safety Rocking Horse, No. 2	90/-	67/6			**MILK FLOATS.**			
	c	"Sportiboy" Safety Rocking Horse, No. 3	120/-	90/-	43	2365	OO Milk Float	5/4	
	d	"Sportiboy" Safety Rocking Horse, No. 4	150/-	112/6		2366	W „ „	6/8	
	e	"Sportiboy" Safety Rocking Horse, No. 5	224/-	168/-		2367	X „ „	16/-	
	f	"Sportiboy" Safety Rocking Horse, No. 6	308/-	231/-		2368	O „ „	11/10	8/11
						b	A „ „	21/4	15/11
		DOUBLE-SIDED ROCKERS AND PUSH HORSE.				c	B „ „	28/-	21/-
	2344	Royal Jumbo Rocker	26/-	19/6			**TRADESMAN'S BARROWS.**			
	2345	Cock-a-do Rocker	14/-	10/6		2370	Baker's Barrow No. O, no bread	14/	10/6
	2346	Shaggy Rocker	33/4	25/-		2369	„ „ „ 1	39/4	29/6
	2347	Mister Quack Rocker	36/8	27/6			Extra Loaves ... per doz.	20/-	
	2348	Swan Rocker	33/4	25/-			„ Cakes „	5/-	
	2349	Double Push Horse	26/-	19/6		2371	G.P.O. „	33/4	25/-
						2372	Ice Cream Barrow No. 1	9/4	6/11
		BLACKBOARDS AND EASELS.				b	„ „ „ 2	16/8	12/6
41	2350	Size O, 12 in a box	1/-				Ice Cream Tricycle	140/-	105/-
	2351	„ A, 12 „	1/4				**BARREL ORGANS.**			
	2352	„ 1 each in a strong paper bag	2/8			2373	Barrel Organ "A"	16/8	12/6
	b	„ 2 „ „ „	3/4			b	„ „ "B"	28/-	21/-
	c	„ 3 „ „ „	5/-				**COLD FRAME AND GREEN-HOUSES.**			
	d	„ 4 „ „ „	7/-		44	2374	Cold Frame	12/8	9/6
	2353	„ 6, Coloured Easel, each in a strong paper bag	5/4	3/11		2375	Greenhouse No. 1	28/-	21/-
	b	„ 7, Coloured Easel, each in a strong paper bag	6/8	4/11		2376	„ „ 2	46/8	35/-
	c	„ 8, Coloured Easel, each in a strong paper bag	9/4	6/11			**GARDEN TOYS.**			
						2375a	Garden Roller No. 1	7/4	5/6
		POLE CARTS, DUMP CARTS, AND PORTER'S TROLLEYS.				b	„ „ 2	8/8	6/6
	2354	"A" Wood Pole Cart	5/4			c	„ „ 3	11/4	8/6
	2355	1 Sand Pole Carts	6/-			2376a	Elm Garden Wagon	33/4	25/-
	b	2 „ „	8/-			2377	Garden Cart No. 1	26/-	19/6
	c	3 „ „	10/-			2378	„ „ „ 2	52/8	39/6
	2356	No. 1 Two Wheel Dump Cart	7/10	5/11		2379	Farm Wagon No. 1	26/-	19/6
	b	„ 2 „ „ „ „ adjustable handle	10/-	7/6		b	„ „ „ 2	30/-	22/6
	c	„ 3 Two Wheel Dump Cart, adjustable handle	14/-	10/6		c	„ „ „ 3	36/8	27/6
	2357	O Porter's Trolley	3/10	2/11			**DUMP WAGON DE LUXE.**			
	b	1 „ „	5/4	3/11		2380	Dump Wagon de Luxe No. 1	8/8	6/6
	c	2 „ „	7/4	5/6		b	„ „ „ „ „ 2	12/8	9/6
	2358	Tubular Porter's Trolley	4/4			c	„ „ „ „ „ 3	16/8	12/6
							DOLLS' COTS.			
		TRI-ANG BRICK TRUCKS AND WAGONS.			45	2381	OO Doll's Cot	8/-	
42	2359	No. 0 Tri-ang Brick Truck	2/8	1/11		2382	X „ „	9/-	
	b	„ 1 „ „ „	4/-	2/11		2383	1 „ „	14/-	10/6
	c	„ 2 „ „ „	10/-	7/6		2384	2 „ „	20/-	15/-
	2360	Tri-ang Brick Wagon	9/4	6/11		2385	3 „ „	23/4	17/6
						2386	2F Folding Doll's Cot	23/4	17/6
		WHEELBARROWS.				2387	3F „ „ „	30/-	22/6
	2361	Pine Barrow "A," packed 2 in a box	5/-			2388	4 Doll' Cot	39/4	29/6
	b	„ „ "B," „ „	6/-			2389	Cosy Cot No. 1	5/6	
	c	„ „ "C," „ „	7/-			b	„ „ „ 2	7/6	
	d	„ „ "D," „ „	8/-				**KITCHENETTES, DRESSERS, LAUNDRY SETS.**			
	e	„ „ "E," „ „	10/-		46	2390	No. 1 Kitchenette	10/8	7/11
	2362	Wood Barrow W, packed 2 in a box	3/6			2391	„ 2 „	30/-	22/6
	b	„ „ X, „ „	5/-			2392	„ 3 „	66/-	49/6
	c	„ „ Y „	6/-			2393	Scullery Sink	60/-	45/-
	d	„ „ Z „	7/-			2394	No. 1 Toy Dresser	6/8	5/-
						b	„ 1C „ „ (coloured)	10/-	7/6
						2395	Laundry Set	21/4	15/11
						2396	Tri-ang Wringer	10/-	7/6

Page in Illustrated List	Index Reference No.	ARTICLE.	Price.	Maintained Advtd. Retail Selling Price
		Tri-ang Tricycles Front Wheel Drive (contd.)		
Page 4	b	Tri-ang Junior Tricycle, No. 601S ...	39/4	29/6
	c	" " " 602S ...	44/8	33/6
	2544	Tri-ang Trike No. 1	56/-	42/-
	b	" " " 2	60/-	45/-
	c	" " " 3	63/4	47/6
	d	" " " 4	66/-	49/6
	2545	Tot Trike No. 500	18/-	
	b	" " " 501	19/6	
	c	" " " 502	21/-	
	2546	Tot Carrier Trike ...	33/4	25/-
	2547	No. 3 Tri-ang Tip Carrier Tricycle ...	106/-	79/6
	2548	Xercycle	9/2	6/11
Sectional Catalogue No. 37b		**MINIC all to Scale Clockwork TOYS**		
Page 2 & 3	2549	Ford Saloon	8d.	6d.
	2550	" Royal Mail	8d.	6d.
	2551	" Light Delivery Van ...	8d.	6d.
	2552	Sports Saloon	1/4	1/-
	2553	Limousine	1/4	1/-
	2554	Cabriolet ...	1/4	1/-
	2555	Town Coupe	1/4	1/-
	2556	Open Touring Car ...	1/4	1/-
	2557	Streamline Saloon ...	1/4	1/-
	2558	" Sports	1/4	1/-
	2559	Learner's Car ...	1/4	1/-
	2560	Racing Car	1/4	1/-
	2561	Tractor	1/4	1/-
	2562	Delivery Lorry	1/4	1/-
	2563	Petrol Tank Lorry ...	1/4	1/-
	2564	Tri-ang Transport Van ...	1/8	1/3
	2565	C. P. Van	1/8	1/3
	2566	Tip Lorry	1/8	1/3
	2567	Luton Tri-ang Transport ...	2/-	1/6
	2568	Lorry with Cases	2/-	1/6
	2569	Light Tank	2/-	1/6
	2570	Steamroller	2/-	1/6
	2571	Mechanical Horse and Pantechnicon	2/8	2/-
	2572	" " " Fuel Oil Trailer	2/8	2/-
	2573	Tractor and Trailer with Cases ...	2/8	2/-
	2574	Dust Cart	2/8	2/-
	2575	Mechanical Horse, Trailer and Cases	3/4	2/6
	2576	Breakdown Lorry	4/8	3/6
	2577	Searchlight Lorry, with electric light	4/8	3/6
	2578	Single Deck Bus (red or green) ...	4/8	3/6
	2579	Rolls Type Open Sports, with electric headlamps and battery ...	4/8	3/6
	2580	Double Deck Bus (Red or Green) ...	6/8	5/-
	2581	Fire Engine, with electric headlamps and battery ...	10/-	7/6
	2582	Caravan Trailer, with electric light ...	4/8	3/6
		Batteries for Minics fitted with electric light ... ... per doz.	6/-	
		MINIC PRESENTATION SETS.		
Page 4	2583	No. 1 Minic Presentation Set ...	6/8	5/-
	2584	" 2 " " ...	14/-	10/6
		MINIC CONSTRUCTION SET.		
	2585	Minic Construction Set No. 1 ...	20/-	15/-
		FILLING, SERVICE AND FIRE STATIONS		
Page 5	2586	No. OO Filling Station	1/4	
	2587	" O "	2/-	1/6
	2588	" 1 Service Station, with elec. lights	5/4	3/11
	2589	" 2 " " " "	6/8	5/-
	2590	" 3 " " " "	10/-	7/6
	2591	" 4 " " " "	20/-	15/-
	2592	" 5 " " " "	33/4	25/-
	2593	" 1 Fire Station (not illus.) ...	6/8	5/-
	2594	" 1E " " with elec. light ...	14/-	10/6
		Minic Display Stands, with Beacons only	6/8	5/-
		Minic Display Stand, with electric Traffic Signals and Beacons, fitted and wired (no transformer)	39/4	29/6
		Minic Show Stand	5/-	

Page in Illustrated List	Index Reference No.	ARTICLE.	Price.	Maintained Advtd. Retail Selling Price
		TRI-ANG LARGE SIZE CLOCKWORK CARS AND VANS		
Page 6	2595	Magic Midget	6/8	5/-
	2596	No. 1 Saloon	8/-	5/11
	2597	" 1E " 2 electric lights	9/4	6/11
	2598	" 1 Sports	8/-	5/11
	2599	" 1E " 2 electric lights	9/4	6/11
	2600	203/4 Steam Box Van	6/8	4/11
	a	203/4E " " " 2 elec. lights	8/-	5/11
	2601	200/4 " Tipping Lorry ...	6/8	4/11
	b	200/4E " " " 2 elec. lights	8/-	5/11
	2602	103/4 Motor Delivery Van ...	6/8	4/11
	c	103/4E " " " 2 elec. lights	8/-	5/11
	2603	100/4 " Tipping Lorry ...	6/8	4/11
	e	100/4E " " " 2 elec. lights	8/-	5/11
	2604	300/4 Trailer	2/8	1/11
		CLOCKWORK LORRIES, VANS, ETC.		
Page 7	2605	60/1 Steam Tip Lorry	1/4	1/-
	2606	61/1 " Dust Cart	1/4	1/-
	2607	62/1 " Milk Tanker	1/4	1/-
	2608	63/1 " Box Van	1/4	1/-
	2609	50/1 Motor Tip Lorry	1/4	1/-
	2610	51/1 Motor Dust Cart	1/4	1/-
	2611	52/1 " Petrol Tanker ...	1/4	1/-
	2612	53/1 " Box Van	1/4	1/-
	2613	500/1 Trailer	8d.	6d.
	2614	Motor Lorry Fleet	8/-	5/11
	2615	Steam " "	8/-	5/11
	2616	54/0 Clockwork Saloon ...	8d.	6d.
	2617	54/1 " "		
	2618	54/1E " " 2 elec. lights	2/8	1/11
		CLOCKWORK TANKS AND TRACTORS		
Page 8	2619	No. 1 Tractor	8d.	6d.
	2620	" 2 "	3/4	
	2621	" 1 Tank	8d.	6d.
	2622	" 2 "Tiger" Tank	5/4	3/11
	2623	No. 1 Farm Tractor	1/-	9d.
	2624	" 1 " " and Trailer ...	1/4	1/-
	2625	" 2 " "	3/4	2/6
	2626	" 2 " " and Trailer	4/8	3/6
Sectional Catalogue No. 37c		**FROG MODEL AIRCRAFT.**		
Page 1	2627	Frog Interceptor Mk. IV, British or foreign markings ...	6/8	5/-
	b	Frog Interceptor Mk. IV, with Squadron markings	10/-	7/6
	2628	Squadron markings for Frog Mk. IV (per Set)	2/-	1/6
	2629	Ski-Plane	10/-	7/6
	2630	Hangar No. 1, Frog Mk. IV ...	6/8	5/-
Page 2	2631	De Havilland Leopard Moth Construction Kit	3/4	2/6
	2632	De Havilland Hornet Moth Construction Kit	4/8	3/6
	2633	The Hawker "Demon" Construction Kit	6/-	4/6
	2634	The Miles "Hawk Major" Construction Kit	14/-	10/6
Page 3	2635	Hawker Hart Mk. 2 Day Bomber ...	56/-	42/-
	2636	Puss Moth Monoplane	23/4	17/6
	2637	Hangar No. 2, for Hawker, Hart and Puss Moth	14/-	10/6
Page 4	2638	The Silver Arrow	3/4	2/6
	b	Geared up Hand Winder for Silver Arrow	1/4	1/-
	2639	Meteor	6/8	5/-
	2640	Mercury	16/8	12/6
	2641	Electrostatic Aeroplane	3/4	2/6
		Foil Gliders for Electrostatic Aeroplane, per box of 12	8d.	6d.
	2642	The Tadpole	3/4	2/6
	2643	The Bantam	3/4	2/6
	2644	The Tern	2/-	1/6
	2645	Frog Lubricant ... per doz.	2/8	2/-

ALPHABETICAL INDEX

FROG MODEL AIRCRAFT

ILLUSTRATED AND DESCRIBED IN SECTIONAL CATALOGUE No. 39A

★ SPECIAL NOTE

Tri-ang Mickey Mouse Toys and Nursery Furniture are only available for Export to Countries in the British Empire.

Tri-ang Toys

REGD TRADE MARK

Regd. Trade Mark.

The finest Toys for Girls or Boys !